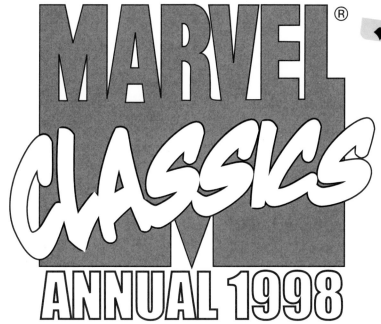

The Time: August 1961. The Place: a corner newsstand. Racked alongside the other comics is a new title: THE FANTASTIC FOUR.

A new comic - so what? Comics had been popular back in the 40s and 50s but, by 1961, any kid wanting a swift dose of action and adventure only had to turn on the TV, sit back and enjoy the show. Comic book sales were falling out of sight. The public had lost interest in the old characters and publishers tried in vain to re-capture their readership's imagination with new heroes. If THE FANTASTIC FOUR wanted to stick around for more than a handful of issues, it would have to be something different.

It was. Over thirty years later, Reed Richards, Sue Storm, Johnny Storm and Aunt Petunia's favourite nephew, Ben Grimm are still busy saving the world on a monthly basis. And they're not alone. Spider-Man, The Incredible Hulk, Iron Man, The Mighty Thor and The X-Men are just a few of the costumed superheroes to have joined them on the shelves of comic shops around the world. Copies of the earliest issues command fantastic sale-room prices and the characters have moved beyond the flimsy four-colour medium that spawned them onto trading cards, television and film.

Why? The answer lies in the characters themselves. They not only fought the villains provided for them each month by the writers and artists, they fought amongst themselves, they had problems at home, their love-lives were a mess and they never seemed to get the credit they deserved for going up against the latest super-powered menace. Being able to demolish a building with a single punch, climb up the side of a skyscraper or shoot ray-beams from your eyes didn't make life any easier for these guys. If anything, it made life even more complicated than it already was! This struck a chord with the comics readers of the time and they demanded more.

As more characters were added to the roster, the Marvel Universe began to emerge: a place in which any or all of the readers' favourite heroes and villains could co-exist and interact. It provided the backdrop for a thousand schoolyard speculations: Who was stronger - The Hulk or The Thing? Who could fly faster - The Human Torch or The Angel? Over time, characters and costumes changed, storylines grew darker, less optimistic and interwove to a fantastic degree. But that is all in the future. Between these covers, Reed Richards' rocket is on the launch pad, an insignificant spider is dangling on a thread between two electrodes and, unbeknownst to the world, heroes are waiting to be born.

This is how it all began...

THE FANTASTIC FOUR

When their attempt to become the first humans in space goes wrong, Reed Richards, Sue Richards, Johnny Storm and Ben Grimm find themselves possessed of fantastic powers. Taking the names Mr. Fantastic, The Invisible Girl, The Human Torch and The Thing, they fight menaces from deep beneath the earth and beyond the stars!
(First Appearance: THE FANTASTIC FOUR #1. November 1961.)

SPIDER-MAN

Once Bitten by a radioactive spider, shy bookworm Peter Parker gains a proportional agility and strength. Able to cling to any surface and possessing a web-spinning device of his own design, he fights crime in a city that has branded him a menace!
(First Appearance: AMAZING FANTASY #15. August 1962.)
Also included here is Spiderman's first appearance in his own comic.

THE INCREDIBLE HULK

Scientist Bruce Banner becomes the first victim of his own Gamma Bomb, causing him to turn into a green-skinned monster of incredible strength. A terrifying rage burns within him and "...the angrier Hulk gets, the stronger Hulk becomes!"
(First Appearance: THE INCREDIBLE HULK #1. May 1962.)

THE AVENGERS

Iron Man, Thor, Ant-Man and The Wasp join forces to save the world from The Hulk's rampage... and a new superhero team is born!
(First Appearance: THE AVENGERS #1. September 1963.)

THE X-MEN

Mutants, born with powers beyond the merely human, brought together by the wheelchair-bound Professor Xavier and trained to protect a world that hates and fears them!
(First Appearance: THE X-MEN #1. September 1963.)

MARVEL® CLASSICS

ANNUAL 1998

£6.99

M61

Marvel Classics Annual is published
under licence from Marvel Characters Inc.
by

Pedigree Books
The Old Rectory, Matford Lane,
Exeter EX2 4PS

ISBN: 1-874507-775

DR. REED RICHARDS · BEN GRIMM · SUSAN STORM · JOHNNY STORM

HERE THEY ARE...

THE FANTASTIC FOUR!

v-372

WITH THE SUDDEN FURY OF A THUNDERBOLT, A FLARE IS SHOT INTO THE SKY OVER CENTRAL CITY! THREE AWESOME WORDS TAKE FORM AS IF BY MAGIC, AND A LEGEND IS BORN.!!

LOOK! IN THE SKY-- WHAT IN BLAZES DOES IT MEAN?

I DUNNO, BUT THE CROWDS ARE GETTIN' PANICKY!

RUMORS ARE FLYIN' ABOUT AN ALIEN INVASION!

ABOVE ALL THE HUBBUB AND EXCITEMENT, ONE STRANGE FIGURE HOLDS A STILL-SMOKING FLARE GUN! ONE STRANGE MAN WHO IS SOMEHOW MORE THAN JUST A MAN--FOR HE IS THE LEADER OF... THE FANTASTIC FOUR!

IT IS THE FIRST TIME I HAVE FOUND IT NECESSARY TO GIVE THE SIGNAL! I PRAY IT WILL BE THE LAST!

1

2

4

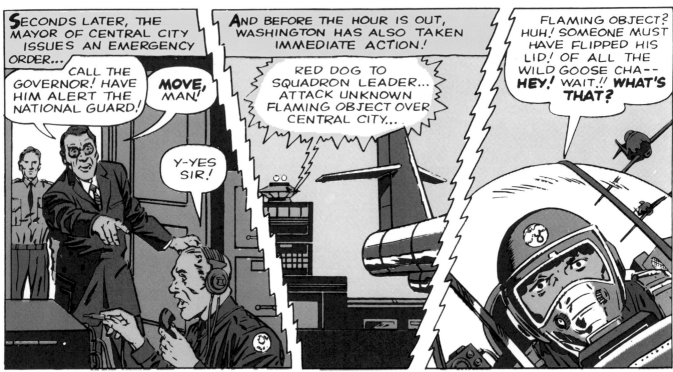

SUDDENLY, THE HUMAN TORCH'S FLAME BEGINS TO DIMINISH... AND, AS THE MISSILE IS ABOUT TO STRIKE HIM, TWO IMPOSSIBLY LONG ARMS REACH ABOVE THE ROOF-TOPS, AND...

GOT IT.!!

MOVING WITH DAZZLING SPEED, ONE OF THE IN-CREDIBLE ARMS HURLS THE MIGHTY MISSILE FAR FROM SHORE, WHERE IT EXPLODES HARMLESSLY OVER THE SEA!

BUT, AS THE FLYING BOY'S FLAME FLICKERS OUT ALTOGETHER, HE BEGINS TO PLUMMET TOWARD EARTH... TOWARD A CERTAIN DOOM.!

GRAB ME, JOHNNY BOY.!! THAT'S IT.!!

WHO IS THIS UNBELIEVABLE STRANGER WHO HAS SAVED THE HUMAN TORCH?

YOU'RE SAFE NOW, LAD.! YOU'RE SAFE!

IN FACT, WHO ARE ALL FOUR OF THESE STRANGE AND ASTONISHING HUMANS? HOW DID THEY BECOME WHAT THEY ARE? WHAT MYSTIC QUIRK OF FATE BROUGHT THEM TOGETHER, TO FORM THE AWE-INSPIRING GROUP KNOWN AS THE FANTASTIC FOUR??

YOU ALL HEEDED MY SUMMONS.!! GOOD.!! THERE IS A TASK THAT AWAITS US... A FEARFUL TASK!

8

BUT, THERE IS TIME ENOUGH TO LEARN OF THE TASK WHICH FACES THE FANTASTIC FOUR! FIRST, LET US DISCOVER **MORE** ABOUT THEIR ORIGIN-- LET US GO BACK TO THAT MOMENTOUS DAY WHEN AN ANGRY BEN GRIMM CONFRONTED DR. REED RICHARDS...

IF YOU WANT TO FLY TO THE STARS, THEN **YOU** PILOT THE SHIP! COUNT **ME** OUT!

YOU **KNOW** WE HAVEN'T DONE ENOUGH RESEARCH INTO THE EFFECT OF COSMIC RAYS! THEY MIGHT KILL US ALL OUT IN SPACE!

BEN, WE'VE **GOT** TO TAKE THAT CHANCE... UNLESS WE WANT THE COMMIES TO BEAT US TO IT!

I-- I NEVER THOUGHT THAT **YOU** WOULD BE A COWARD!

A COWARD!! NOBODY CALLS **ME** A COWARD! GET THE SHIP! I'LL FLY HER NO MATTER **WHAT** HAPPENS.!!

AND SO, LED BY A DETERMINED DR. REED RICHARDS, THE LITTLE GROUP SPED TOWARD THE SPACEPORT ON THE OUTSKIRTS OF TOWN!

SUSAN, BEN AND I **KNOW** WHAT WE'RE DOING... BUT YOU-- AND JOHNNY...

DON'T SAY IT, REED! I'M YOUR FIANCÉE! WHERE **YOU** GO, I GO!

AND **I'M** TAGGIN' ALONG WITH SIS-- SO IT'S SETTLED!

NO TIME TO WAIT FOR OFFICIAL CLEARANCE! CONDITIONS ARE RIGHT TONIGHT! **LET'S GO!**

BEFORE THE GUARD CAN STOP THEM, THE MIGHTY SHIP WHICH REED RICHARDS HAD SPENT YEARS CONSTRUCTING IS SOARING INTO THE HEAVENS...TOWARDS OUTER SPACE!

SHE'S BEHAVING LIKE A BABY! EVERYTHING IS PERFECT!

YEAH, EXCEPT THE COSMIC RAYS! NO ONE KNOWS WHAT **THEY'LL** DO....

9

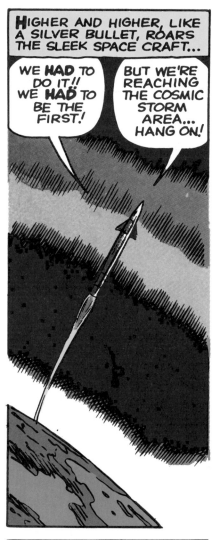

AT THAT MOMENT, THE POWERFUL SHIP'S AUTOMATIC PILOT TOOK OVER, AND MANAGED TO RETURN THE SLEEK ROCKET SAFELY TO EARTH, IN A ROUGH, BUT NON-FATAL LANDING!

I--I'M GRATEFUL WE'RE ALL ALIVE!! IT WAS MIGHTY CLOSE!

BUT, REED...WE FAILED!! AFTER ALL YOUR WORK... YOUR DEDICATION... WE FAILED!

BAH! WHAT'D YOU EXPECT?

BUT WE'RE STILL NOT COMPLETELY SAFE! WE STILL HAVE TO SEE WHETHER THE COSMIC RAYS AFFECTED US IN ANY WAY!

OH, REED... I FEEL SO STRANGE!

SUSAN! LOOK AT SUSAN!!

WHAT'S WRONG?

YOU'RE =GASP= FADING AWAY!!

OH, NO!! NO!!

IT'S IMPOSSIBLE!

SOMEHOW THE COSMIC RAYS HAVE ALTERED YOUR ATOMIC STRUCTURE... MAKING YOU GROW INVISIBLE!

SIS! I CAN'T SEE YOU AT ALL ANY MORE!

HOW... HOW LONG WILL IT LAST?

THERE'S NO WAY OF KNOWING!!

WHA--WHAT IF SHE NEVER GETS VISIBLE AGAIN??

LOOK!! I SEE HER!

I'M MYSELF AGAIN! IT HAPPENED SO SUDDENLY...ALL BY ITSELF!

11

YOU'VE TURNED INTO **MONSTERS**... BOTH OF YOU.!! IT'S THOSE RAYS! THOSE TERRIBLE COSMIC RAYS!

NOW I KNOW WHY I'VE BEEN FEELING SO WARM! LOOK AT **ME**!! THEY'VE AFFECTED ME, TOO! WHEN I GET EXCITED I CAN FEEL MY BODY BEGIN TO BLAZE!

I'M LIGHTER THAN AIR!! I CAN **FLY**!! LOOK... I **CAN FLY**!!

MINUTES LATER, JOHNNY STORM'S FLAME SUBSIDED AND HE LANDED NEAR THE OTHER THREE! SILENTLY THEY WATCHED THE SMALL FIRE HE HAD STARTED IN THE UNDERBRUSH BURN ITSELF OUT!! SILENTLY THEY WERE EACH OCCUPIED WITH THEIR OWN STARTLING THOUGHTS!

WE'VE **CHANGED**! ALL OF US! WE'RE **MORE** THAN JUST HUMAN!

LISTEN TO ME, **ALL** OF YOU! THAT MEANS **YOU** TOO, BEN! TOGETHER WE HAVE MORE POWER THAN ANY HUMANS HAVE EVER POSSESSED!

YOU DON'T HAVE TO MAKE A SPEECH, BIG SHOT! WE UNDERSTAND! WE'VE GOTTA **USE** THAT POWER TO HELP MANKIND, RIGHT?

RIGHT, BEN, RIGHT!

I'M CALLING MYSELF **THE HUMAN TORCH**-- AND I'M WITH YOU ALL THE WAY!

SAME GOES FOR **ME**... THE **INVISIBLE GIRL**!

THERE'S ONLY **ONE** STILL MISSING... BEN!!

I AIN'T BEN ANYMORE-- I'M WHAT SUSAN CALLED ME-- **THE THING**!!

AND I'LL CALL MYSELF... MISTER FANTASTIC!!

AND SO WAS BORN *"THE FANTASTIC FOUR!!"* AND FROM THAT MOMENT ON, THE WORLD WOULD NEVER AGAIN BE THE SAME!!

·13·

THE FANTASTIC FOUR MEET THE MOLE MAN!

AND NOW, HAVING MET OUR FOUR AMAZING CHARACTERS, LET US RESUME OUR TALE...

I CALLED YOU TOGETHER BECAUSE I HAVE SOME PICTURES TO SHOW YOU!

PICTURES?

WHAT ARE THEY... PIN-UPS?

LOOK! ALL OF YOU! THIS USED TO BE AN ATOMIC PLANT BEHIND THE IRON CURTAIN!

WOW! WHAT HAPPENED TO IT?

14

THE SAME THING THAT HAPPENED TO THE **OTHER** ATOMIC PLANTS ON THOSE PHOTOS!

THIS ONE IS IN **AUSTRALIA**!

AND **THIS** IS IN SOUTH AMERICA!

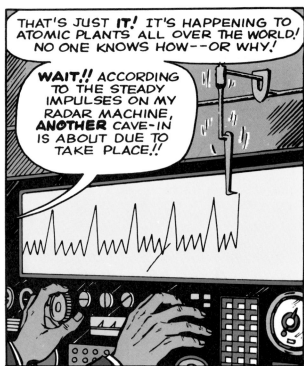

THAT'S JUST **IT!** IT'S HAPPENING TO ATOMIC PLANTS ALL OVER THE WORLD! NO ONE KNOWS HOW--OR WHY!

WAIT!! ACCORDING TO THE STEADY IMPULSES ON MY RADAR MACHINE, **ANOTHER** CAVE-IN IS ABOUT DUE TO TAKE PLACE.!!

AND, EVEN AS REED RICHARDS SPEAKS, HALF-WAY AROUND THE WORLD, IN FRENCH AFRICA, THE FOLLOWING SCENE IS TAKING PLACE...

WHAT IS WRONG, PIERRE?

I DO NOT KNOW! IT SOUNDS INSANE, BUT THE SAND BENEATH MY FEET SEEMS TO BE **THROBBING**!

...ALMOST AS IF SOMETHING IS **MOVING** BELOW US! ALMOST AS IF... LISTEN! DON'T YOU FEEL IT??

RUMBLE RUMBLE

HELP!!

RUMBLE ROAR

IT IS AN **EARTHQUAKE**! BUT HERE IN THE DESERT?? **IMPOSSIBLE!!**

IMPOSSIBLE OR NOT, PIERRE ALMOST FELL TO HIS DOOM!

WAIT!! THE GROUND IS TREMBLING AGAIN!! WHAT CAN IT BE??

SACRE BLEU!! THE EARTH IS GOING **MAD**!!

ROOOOOOMM

15

THE ENTIRE INSTALLATION.!! IT--IT IS CAVING IN!

RRROOMM

BUT THE WORST IS YET TO COME!! FOR, LESS THAN THIRTY SECONDS LATER...

IN THE NAME OF HEAVEN.!!

WHAT IS THAT?

WHAT INDEED?? IT IS A GIGANTIC PAIR OF CLAWS, THE LIKE OF WHICH HAVE NEVER BEEN SEEN ON EARTH, OR ON ANY PLANET IN THE UNIVERSE!! IT IS UNBELIEVABLE... MIND STAGGERING...BUT REAL!

ARTILLERY!! BRING THE ARTILLERY!! HURRY! HURRY!

ARTILLERY! OF WHAT USE IS ARTILLERY AGAINST A CREATURE WHOSE HIDE IS POWERFUL ENOUGH TO DIG ITS WAY UP THRU COUTLESS TONS OF ROCK-HARD EARTH??

ARTILLERY! OF WHAT USE IS ARTILLERY AGAINST A MONSTER WHO CAN CRUSH A HEAVY TANK WITH ONE HAND??

BUT, JUST AS IT SEEMS THAT NOTHING IN THE WORLD WILL HALT THE NIGHTMARE MENACE, THE SHRILL SOUND OF A COMMANDING VOICE IS HEARD... AND THE GOLIATH STOPS IN ITS TRACKS!

ENOUGH! RETURN TO EARTH'S CORE! OUR MISSION HERE IS FINISHED! GO!!

FOR EVEN SUCH A MONSTER HEEDS ITS MASTER! A MASTER KNOWN AS... THE MOLEMAN!!

16

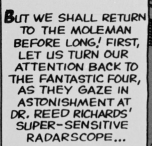

BUT WE SHALL RETURN TO THE MOLEMAN BEFORE LONG! FIRST, LET US TURN OUR ATTENTION BACK TO THE FANTASTIC FOUR, AS THEY GAZE IN ASTONISHMENT AT DR. REED RICHARDS' SUPER-SENSITIVE RADARSCOPE...

THERE! IT HAS HAPPENED AGAIN! THIS TIME IN FRENCH EQUITORIAL AFRICA!

BUT HOW? WHY?

THAT'S WHAT WE'VE GOT TO FIND OUT!

BY STUDYING THE CAVE-INS CAREFULLY, I'VE PIN-POINTED AN ISLAND LOCATED EXACTLY BETWEEN THEM! THAT IS WHERE WE WILL FIND OUR ANSWER! IT IS KNOWN AS MONSTER ISLE!

MONSTER ISLE! THAT'S JUST A FAIRY TALE! THERE'S NO SUCH PLACE!

ONLY ONE WAY TO FIND OUT, BEN!

AND FIND OUT THEY DO! HOURS LATER, ABOARD THEIR SMALL, PRIVATE JET, THE FANTASTIC FOUR SEE A STRANGE MOUNTAIN RISING FROM THE SEA, LIKE AN UNEARTHLY GROTESQUE FACE!! THEY HAVE FOUND... MONSTER ISLE!

THERE IT IS!

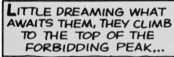

LITTLE DREAMING WHAT AWAITS THEM, THEY CLIMB TO THE TOP OF THE FORBIDDING PEAK...

IF THIS IS JUST A WILD GOOSE CHASE, MISTER, I'LL MAKE SURE YOU LIVE TO REGRET IT!

SAVE YOUR BREATH FOR THE CLIMB, GRUESOME!

HOLD IT!! I HEAR SOMETHING!!

IT'S COMING FROM BELOW!

LOOK!! THOSE EYES...

SUDDENLY, A LIVING THREE-HEADED NIGHTMARE HURLS ITSELF AT THEM FROM OVER THE EDGE OF THE PEAK OF MONSTER ISLE!

17

QUICK, SUE! **TURN INVISIBLE!**

SEEING ONE OF ITS INTENDED VICTIMS VANISH BEFORE ITS EYES, THE MONSTER HALTS... BEWILDERED!!

THERE'S JUST TIME FOR ME TO BECOME **MR. FANTASTIC** AGAIN! I'LL MAKE A HUGE LASSO OUT OF MY ARM!

GOT 'IM!!

I HAD **HEARD** THERE WAS A GIANT THREE-HEADED CREATURE GUARDING THIS ISLE... BUT HE SHALL GUARD IT NO LONGER!!

BUT BEFORE MR. FANTASTIC AND THE HUMAN TORCH CAN CATCH THEIR BREATH...

LOOK OUT!!

IT'S A CAVE-IN!

HOLD ON, JOHNNY! **HOLD ON!**

≡GULP!≡ LUCKY SUE AND BEN WEREN'T WITH US AT THE EDGE!

18

19

THE MOLEMAN'S SECRET!

BEFORE WE WITNESS THE BREATH-TAKING CON-CLUSION OF OUR AMAZING TALE, LET US GATHER TOGETHER ALL THE LOOSE ENDS! LET US RETURN TO THE TWO MEMBERS OF THE FANTASTIC FOUR WHO DID NOT FALL BELOW DURING THE CAVE-IN...

REED... AND JOHNNY... GOT TO FIND THEM!!

WAIT! THAT NOISE--BEHIND ME!! WHAT--??

BUT OTHER EARS ALSO HEAR THE MENACING SOUNDS... AND OTHER EYES BEHOLD THE FRIGHTENING SIGHT...

THE EYES OF... THE THING!!

DUCK, SUE! OUT OF THE WAY!

LET ME HANDLE 'IM!

20

THE SECOND GIGANTIC GUARDIAN OF MONSTER ISLE IS POWERFUL BEYOND BELIEF...BUT HE IS FIGHTING AN ENEMY WHOSE EVERY ATOM HAS BEEN CHARGED WITH COSMIC RAYS...AN ENEMY WHO **CAN'T BE STOPPED!**

YOU'VE DONE IT, BEN! YOU'VE BEATEN HIM!

WHAT DID YOU **EXPECT??**

I'M **THE THING,** AIN'T I??

NOW LET'S GO AND FIND THAT SKINNY, LOUD-MOUTHED BOY-FRIEND OF YOURS!

OH, BEN--IF ONLY YOU COULD STOP HATING REED FOR WHAT HAPPENED TO YOU!

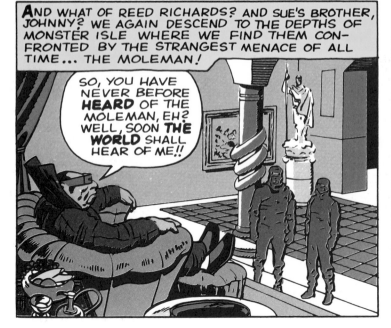

AND WHAT OF REED RICHARDS? AND SUE'S BROTHER, JOHNNY? WE AGAIN DESCEND TO THE DEPTHS OF MONSTER ISLE WHERE WE FIND THEM CONFRONTED BY THE STRANGEST MENACE OF ALL TIME... THE MOLEMAN!

SO, YOU HAVE NEVER BEFORE **HEARD** OF THE MOLEMAN, EH? WELL, SOON **THE WORLD** SHALL HEAR OF ME!!

FOR SOON, THE MOLEMAN WILL HAVE THE ENTIRE WORLD IN HIS **POWER!**

HOW DID YOU **GET** HERE? WHAT **IS** THIS PLACE?

21

"IT ALL STARTED LONG AGO!! BECAUSE THE PEOPLE OF THE SURFACE WORLD MOCKED ME!"

WHAT? **ME** GO OUT WITH **YOU?** DON'T MAKE ME LAUGH!

I **KNOW** YOU'RE QUALIFIED, BUT YOU CAN'T WORK HERE! YOU'D SCARE OUR OTHER EMPLOYEES AWAY!

HEY, IS THAT YOUR FACE, OR ARE YOU WEARIN' A MASK? HAW HAW!

"FINALLY, I COULD STAND IT NO LONGER! I DECIDED TO STRIKE OUT ALONE...TO SEARCH FOR A NEW WORLD ...THE LEGENDARY LAND AT THE CENTER OF THE EARTH! A WORLD WHERE I COULD BE KING! MY TRAVELS TOOK ME ALL OVER THE GLOBE..."

EVEN THIS LONELINESS IS BETTER THAN THE CRUELTY OF MY FELLOW MEN!

"AND THEN, JUST WHEN I HAD ALMOST ABANDONED HOPE... WHEN MY LITTLE SKIFF HAD BEEN WASHED ASHORE HERE ON MONSTER ISLE, **I FOUND IT!**"

THAT STRANGE CAVERN! WHERE CAN IT LEAD TO?

"I SOON **SAW** WHERE IT LED... IT LED TO THE LAND OF MY DREAMS..."

DOWN THERE... BELOW-- **I'VE FOUND IT!!** IT'S EARTH'S CENTER!

"BUT IN THE DREAD SILENCE OF THAT HUGE CAVERN, THE SUDDEN SHOCK OF MY LOUD OUTCRY CAUSED A VIOLENT AVALANCHE, AND..."

"...WHEN IT WAS OVER, I HAD SOMEHOW MIRACULOUSLY SURVIVED THE FALL... BUT, DUE TO THE IMPACT OF THE CRASH, I HAD LOST MOST OF MY SIGHT! YES, I HAD FOUND THE CENTER OF EARTH--BUT I WAS **STRANDED** HERE...LIKE A HUMAN MOLE!!"

22

THAT WAS TO BE THE LAST OF MY MISFORTUNES! MY LUCK BEGAN TO TURN IN MY FAVOR! I MASTERED THE CREATURES DOWN HERE-- MADE THEM DO MY BIDDING-- AND WITH THEIR HELP, I CARVED OUT AN UNDER-GROUND EMPIRE!

A NOTE OF MADNESS CREEPS INTO THE MOLE'S VOICE AS HE SPEAKS OF HIS POWER! AND THEN, HE MAKES HIS FIRST FATAL MISTAKE...

I CONQUERED EVERYTHING ABOUT ME! I EVEN LEARNED TO SENSE THINGS IN THE DARK--LIKE A MOLE! HERE, I'LL SHOW YOU! TRY TO STRIKE ME WITH THAT POLE! TRY IT, I SAY!!

HAH! I SENSED THAT BLOW COMING! NOTHING CAN TAKE ME BY SURPRISE! AND, I HAVE DEVELOPED OTHER SENSES TOO, LIKE THOSE OF THE BAT--

I POSSESS A NATURAL RADAR SENSE... A WARNING SYSTEM WHICH ENABLES ME TO EVADE WHATEVER DANGER STRIKES AT ME!

COMPARED TO THE MOLE-MAN, YOU ARE SLOW... CLUMSY!! HAH HAH!!

SEE HOW EASILY I DEFEAT YOU... OR ANY OTHERS WHO TRY TO DEFY ME!

NOW, BEFORE I SLAY YOU ALL, BEHOLD MY MASTER PLAN! SEE THIS MAP OF MY UNDERGROUND EMPIRE! EACH TUNNEL LEADS TO A MAJOR CITY! AS SOON AS I HAVE WRECKED EVERY ATOMIC PLANT, EVERY SOURCE OF EARTHLY POWER, MY MIGHTY MOLE CREATURES WILL ATTACK AND DESTROY EVERYTHING THAT LIVES ABOVE THE SURFACE!

AND NOW, AT MY SIGNAL, THOSE CREATURES OF DARKNESS, MY DENIZENS OF EARTH'S CENTER, SHALL DISPOSE OF ALL OF YOU WITLESS INTRUDERS!

WE'LL SEE ABOUT THAT, MOLE!!

THE THING!!

23

24

MOVING LIKE A WELL-OILED FIGHTING MACHINE, THE FANTASTIC FOUR, WITH THE DEADLY MOLEMAN IN THEIR GRASP, RACE FOR THE SURFACE... BUT THEN THEIR EVIL ANTAGONIST SEIZES THE SIGNAL CORD AGAIN, AND...

YOU HAVEN'T WON YET! EVEN **YOU** CAN'T DEFEAT ALL OF MY UNDER-EARTH HORDE!

HURRY, REED... HURRY!

CAN'T YOU EVEN HOLD ON TO ONE LITTLE GUY?

AND THEN THEY COME... LIKE FIGMENTS OF A MAD NIGHTMARE... ROARING, RUNNING, SNARLING... THE MOLEMAN'S ENTIRE ARMY OF UNDERGROUND GARGOYLES!!

BUT THEY HADN'T COUNTED ON THE UNBELIEVABLE POWER OF THE HUMAN TORCH! FLYING BETWEEN HIS FANTASTIC ALLIES AND THE PURSUING HORDE, HE BLAZES A FIERY SWATH WHICH MELTS THE SOFT EARTH...

THIS WILL CAUSE A ROCKSLIDE, SEALING US OFF FROM THOSE CREATURES!

WE DID IT...WE'RE FREE!! AND THE ENTRANCE TO THE MOLEMAN'S EMPIRE IS SEALED FOREVER!

25

MOMENTS LATER...

BUT WHERE **IS** THE MOLEMAN?

I LEFT HIM BEHIND--HE'LL NEVER TROUBLE ANYONE AGAIN!

AND THE WORDS OF MR. FANTASTIC ARE INDEED PROPHETIC... AS, SECONDS LATER...

HE'S DESTROYED THE ENTIRE ISLE! HE'S SEALED HIMSELF BELOW--FOREVER!

IT'S BEST THAT WAY! THERE WAS NO PLACE FOR HIM IN OUR WORLD ...PERHAPS HE'LL FIND PEACE DOWN THERE... I HOPE SO!

I JUST HOPE WE **HAVE** SEEN THE LAST OF HIM!

BUT, WHETHER WE'VE SEEN THE LAST OF THE MOLEMAN OR NOT, WE WILL SEE MUCH MORE OF THE MOST AMAZING QUARTET IN HISTORY, IN THE NEXT GREAT ISSUE OF-- THE FANTASTIC FOUR!! DON'T MISS IT!!

THE END

AS YOU MAY HAVE GATHERED, PETER PARKER WAS FAR FROM BEING THE BIGGEST MAN ON CAMPUS! BUT, HIS UNCLE BEN THOUGHT HE WAS A PRETTY SPECIAL LAD...

YOU'RE NOT FOOLIN' *ME*, PETEY! I KNOW YOU'RE AWAKE -- AND IT'S TIME FOR SCHOOL!

GOSH, UNCLE BEN -- YOU'RE WORSE THAN A ROOM FULL OF ALARM CLOCKS!

AS FOR PETE'S AUNT MAY, SHE THOUGHT THE SUN ROSE AND SET UPON HER NEPHEW!

I COOKED YOUR FAVORITE BREAKFAST, PETEY -- WHEATCAKES!

DON'T FATTEN HIM UP *TOO* MUCH, DEAR! I CAN HARDLY OUT-WRESTLE HIM *NOW*!

THE FACULTY AT MIDTOWN HIGH WAS ALSO FOND OF THE CLEAN-CUT, HARD-WORKING HONOR STUDENT!

KEEP UP THE GOOD WORK, PARKER, AND YOU'RE SURE TO RATE A SCHOLARSHIP WHEN YOU GRADUATE!

I'LL DO MY BEST, SIR!

BUT ALAS, OTHER TEENAGERS CAN SOMETIMES, UNWITTINGLY, BE SO VERY CRUEL TO A SHY YOUNG MAN...

SALLY, I, EH, WAS WONDERING IF YOU'RE BUSY TONIGHT...?

PETER, FOR THE UMPTEENTH TIME, YOU'RE JUST NOT MY TYPE...

...NOT WHEN DREAM BOATS LIKE FLASH THOMPSON ARE AROUND!

I ADMIRE YOUR GOOD TASTE, DOLL! GET LOST, BOOKWORM!

LOOK, THERE'S A GREAT NEW EXHIBIT AT THE SCIENCE HALL TONIGHT! WOULD ANY OF YOU LIKE TO GO WITH ME?

SCIENCE HALL! HAH!

YOU STICK TO SCIENCE, SON! *WE'LL* TAKE THE CHICKS!

YES, FOR SOME, BEING A TEEN-AGER HAS MANY HEART-BREAKING MOMENTS!

SEE YOU AROUND, BOOKWORM!

GIVE OUR REGARDS TO THE ATOM-SMASHERS, PETER!

SOME DAY I'LL SHOW THEM! -SOB- SOME DAY THEY'LL BE SORRY! -- SORRY THAT THEY LAUGHED AT ME!

SCIENCE EXHIBIT

EXPERIMENTS IN RADIOACTIVITY

OPEN TO THE PUBLIC

ROOM 30

2

WHAT'S COME *OVER* ME! I-I'M SCALING THIS WALL JUST AS EASILY AS I CAN *WALK!*

MOMMY! LOOK AT THE MAN WALKING UP THE SIDE OF A BUILDING!

THAT'S THE LAST HORROR MOVIE I TAKE *YOU* TO, YOUNG MAN!

IT'S *INCREDIBLE!* I REACHED THE ROOF IN JUST A FEW SECONDS!

WHAT'S *THIS??* I CRUSHED THIS STEEL PIPE AS THOUGH IT WERE *PAPER!*

IT'S THE *SPIDER!* IT *HAS* TO BE! SOMEHOW -- IN SOME MIRACULOUS WAY, HIS BITE HAS TRANSFERRED HIS OWN POWER -- TO *ME!*

I CAN WALK DOWN THIS CABLE AS EFFORTLESSLY AS THE SPIDER ITSELF CAN GLIDE ALONG ITS WEB!

I-I'VE GOT TO HAVE TIME TO THINK! I'VE GOT TO PLAN *WHAT* TO *DO* WITH THIS UNBELIEVABLE ABILITY WHICH FATE HAS GIVEN ME!

A FEW MINUTES LATER...

HMMM... THIS WILL BE A GOOD CHANCE TO TEST MY POWER AGAIN!

$100 TO THE MAN WHO CAN STAY IN THE RING THREE MINUTES WITH *CRUSHER HOGAN*

FILLED WITH EXCITEMENT, PETE RACES BACK HOME, AND...

I'LL PUT ON SOME OLD CLOTHES, AND LEAVE MY GLASSES HERE! BUT--WHAT IF I FAIL? I DON'T WANT TO BE A LAUGHING STOCK! I-I'LL FIND SOME WAY TO *DISGUISE* MYSELF!

LISTEN, FRIEND, I'M A TV PRODUCER! WITH THAT ACT OF YOURS I CAN MAKE YOU A *FORTUNE!* AND KEEP THE MASK ANGLE -- IT'S GREAT SHOWMANSHIP! HERE'S MY CARD! CALL ME! YOU'D BE A SMASH ON ED SULLIVAN'S SHOW!

THANKS...

LATER, AT HOME AGAIN...

SHOWMANSHIP?? HE HASN'T SEEN *ANYTHING* YET! SINCE I HAVE THE *POWERS* OF A SPIDER, I'LL DESIGN MYSELF A *SPIDER COSTUME!* AND... OH, HI, AUNT MAY!

YOU LOOKED A LITTLE TIRED, PETEY, SO WE BROUGHT YOU SOME CRACKERS AND MILK!

CRACKERS AND MILK! BLESS 'EM-- IF THEY ONLY *KNEW!*

NOW LET'S SEE-- A SPIDER NEEDS A WEB! THIS LITTLE DEVICE SHOULD JUST DO THE TRICK!

I'LL FASTEN ONE TO EACH ARM-- IT'LL OPERATE BY THE SLIGHTEST PRESSURE OF ANY FINGER!

I'LL NEED A NAME --WELL, GUESS *SPIDER-MAN* IS AS GOOD AS ANY! LOOKS PRETTY GOOD, IF I *DO* SAY SO MYSELF!

SO, THEY LAUGHED AT ME FOR BEING A BOOKWORM, EH? WELL, ONLY A SCIENCE MAJOR COULD HAVE CREATED A DEVICE LIKE THIS!

WITH SOME STRONG LIQUID CEMENT AT THE END, I CAN PULL MYSELF UP *ANYWHERE* WITH MY LITTLE WEB!

AND MY COSTUME IS THIN ENOUGH TO WEAR, UNSEEN, UNDER MY STREET CLOTHES!

OKAY, WORLD -- BETTER HANG ONTO YOUR HAT! HERE COMES THE *SPIDER-MAN!*

6

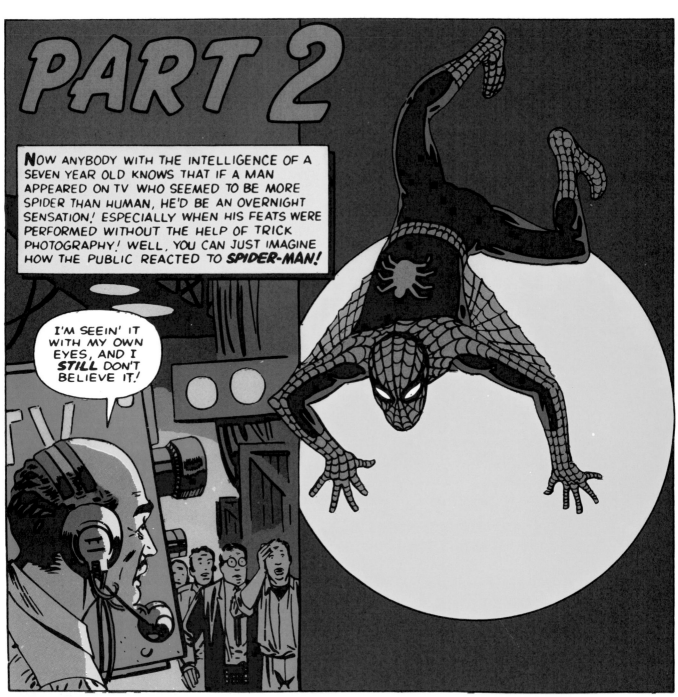

PART 2

NOW ANYBODY WITH THE INTELLIGENCE OF A SEVEN YEAR OLD KNOWS THAT IF A MAN APPEARED ON TV WHO SEEMED TO BE MORE SPIDER THAN HUMAN, HE'D BE AN OVERNIGHT SENSATION! ESPECIALLY WHEN HIS FEATS WERE PERFORMED WITHOUT THE HELP OF TRICK PHOTOGRAPHY! WELL, YOU CAN JUST IMAGINE HOW THE PUBLIC REACTED TO *SPIDER-MAN!*

I'M SEEIN' IT WITH MY OWN EYES, AND I *STILL* DON'T BELIEVE IT!

SURE THEY LOOK AMAZED, INCREDULOUS, AWESTRICKEN! WOULDN'T *YOU???*

AFTER ALL, WHEN WAS THE LAST TIME *YOU* SAW A MAN WITH HIS OWN FANTASTIC SPIDER WEB???

OKAY, SPIDER-MAN --CUT! THAT'S ENOUGH! DON'T SHOW 'EM *TOO MUCH!* LEAVE 'EM BEGGIN' FOR MORE!

7

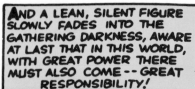

The SECRET of SPIDER-MAN'S MASK

PERHAPS YOU ARE ONE OF THE MANY READERS WHO HAVE WRITTEN US TO ASK WHY SPIDEY'S *EYES* DON'T SHOW THROUGH HIS MASK'S EYELETS? WELL, THERE REALLY *IS* A REASON!

THE WHITE AREAS IN SPIDEY'S EYE CUT-OUTS ON HIS MASK ARE REALLY CLEVER PLASTIC LENSES OF THE TWO-WAY MIRROR TYPE! HE CAN SEE OUT VERY CLEARLY, BUT NO ONE CAN SEE IN! THEREFORE, HE CAN NEVER BE RECOGNIZED BY THE COLOR OF HIS EYES!

THESE INGENIOUS PLASTIC LENSES ALSO PROTECT HIS EYES FROM DUST, DIRT, AND THE GLARE OF THE SUN!

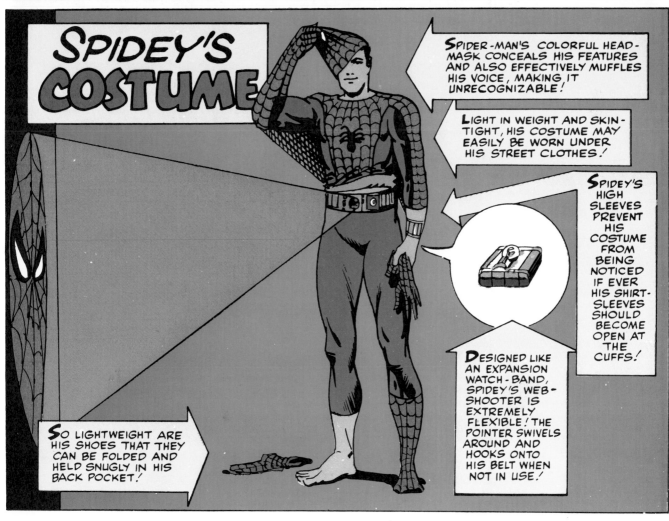

SPIDEY'S COSTUME

SPIDER-MAN'S COLORFUL HEAD-MASK CONCEALS HIS FEATURES AND ALSO EFFECTIVELY MUFFLES HIS VOICE, MAKING IT UNRECOGNIZABLE!

LIGHT IN WEIGHT AND SKIN-TIGHT, HIS COSTUME MAY EASILY BE WORN UNDER HIS STREET CLOTHES!

SPIDEY'S HIGH SLEEVES PREVENT HIS COSTUME FROM BEING NOTICED IF EVER HIS SHIRT-SLEEVES SHOULD BECOME OPEN AT THE CUFFS!

DESIGNED LIKE AN EXPANSION WATCH-BAND, SPIDEY'S WEB-SHOOTER IS EXTREMELY FLEXIBLE! THE POINTER SWIVELS AROUND AND HOOKS ONTO HIS BELT WHEN NOT IN USE!

SO LIGHTWEIGHT ARE HIS SHOES THAT THEY CAN BE FOLDED AND HELD SNUGLY IN HIS BACK POCKET!

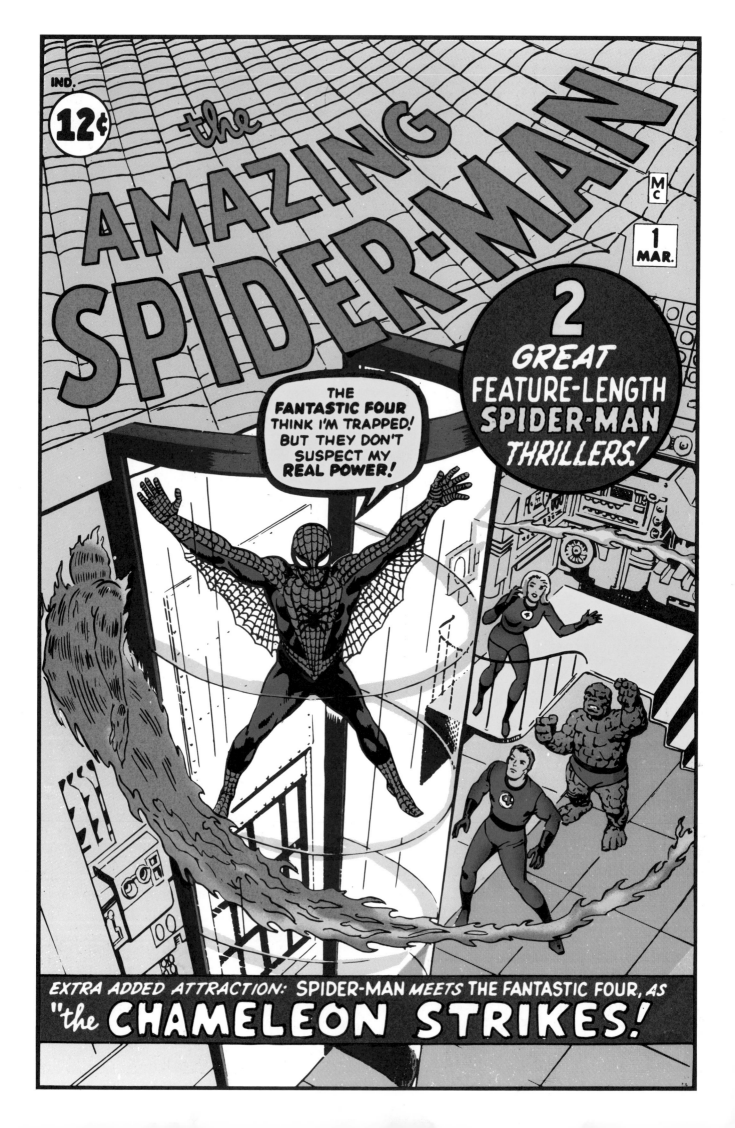

SPIDER-MAN
SCRIPT: STAN LEE • ART: STEVE DITKO • LETTERING: JOHNNY DEE
NOTE: SPIDER-MAN FIRST APPEARED AS A FEATURE IN AMAZING FANTASY #15 AUG.! SO GREAT WAS YOUR RESPONSE VIA LETTERS AND POSTCARDS, THAT IT WAS DECIDED TO GIVE HIM HIS OWN MAGAZINE! A BRIEF SUMMARY FOLLOWS...
FREAK!
PUBLIC MENACE!
SURE, YOU'VE READ MANY STORIES ABOUT MANY DIFFERENT MAGAZINE HEROES! BUT THERE'S NEVER BEEN A STORY LIKE THIS ONE-- BECAUSE THERE'S NEVER BEEN A HERO LIKE---
SPIDER-MAN!
V-816
1

OUR SCENE IS THE BEDROOM OF PETER PARKER, THE TEEN-AGE STUDENT WHOM MANY CONSIDER TO BE A SHY BOOKWORM... BUT, OH, IF THEY ONLY *KNEW!*

UNCLE BEN IS *DEAD!* AND ALL BECAUSE I WAS TOO LATE TO SAVE HIM!

MY SPIDER-MAN COSTUME! I WISH THERE WERE NO SUCH *THING!*

IT ALL STARTED WHEN I WAS BITTEN BY A RADIO-ACTIVE SPIDER...

AND I FOUND MYSELF POSSESSED OF A SPIDER'S *POWERS!* SO I DESIGNED A COSTUME TO GO INTO SHOW BUSINESS AND CASH IN!

OUCH!

BUT WHILE I WAS BUSY SHOWING OFF, AN ARMED BURGLAR FIRED ONE FATAL SHOT AT UNCLE BEN WHEN HE WAS SURPRISED ROBBING OUR HOUSE!"

"AS SOON AS I LEARNED WHAT HAD HAPPENED, I SPED THRU THE CITY VIA MY SPIDER'S WEB, LUSTING FOR VENGEANCE!"

"AND I SOON CAUGHT THE KILLER, AND TURNED HIM OVER TO THE POLICE!"

HE WON'T ESCAPE SPIDERMAN!

GOT YOU!

Y-YOU AIN'T *HUMAN!*

AND NOW, UNCLE BEN IS GONE, AND AUNT MAY AND I ARE ALONE!

AND WHAT'S *WORSE,* WITHOUT UNCLE BEN, WE'VE NO MONEY TO PAY OUR BILLS!

PLEASE GIVE ME A LITTLE MORE TIME! I'LL PAY THE RENT *NEXT* WEEK, IF YOU'LL ONLY WAIT!

2

AND SO... AUNT MAY, THERE'S ONLY *ONE* THING TO DO! I'VE GOT TO QUIT SCHOOL AND GET A JOB!

NO, PETER, YOU MUSTN'T! YOUR UNCLE ALWAYS DREAMED OF YOU BEING A SCIENTIST SOME DAY! YOU *MUST* CONTINUE YOUR STUDIES!

BUT I'VE GOT TO HELP AUNT MAY *SOMEHOW!* WAIT! WITH MY POWERS AS SPIDER-MAN, I CAN DO *ANYTHING!*

"I CAN GO ANYWHERE! NO ONE, NOTHING CAN STOP ME!"

"ANY AMOUNT OF MONEY COULD BE MINE--JUST FOR THE TAKING!"

"BUT *NO!* WHAT AM I THINKING OF ??! I'M NO CRIMINAL! I'M NOT A THIEF! BESIDES, IF I WERE EVER ARRESTED AND IMPRISONED, IT WOULD BREAK AUNT MAY'S HEART!"

NO! THERE'S ONLY ONE OTHER WAY! I'VE GOT TO *PERFORM* AGAIN! I'VE GOT TO BRING MY SPIDER-MAN ACT BEFORE THE PUBLIC ONCE MORE! I'LL CALL A BOOKING AGENT *TONIGHT!*

A FEW DAYS LATER ... AT SCHOOL...

HEY, GANG! *LOOK!* SPIDER-MAN'S GONNA PUT ON A SHOW AT THE TOWN HALL TONIGHT!

AND THE ADMISSION IS ONLY A DOLLAR!

LET'S *ALL* GO!

COUNT *ME* OUT, KIDS! I CAN'T MAKE IT!

WE MIGHT HAVE KNOWN! *HE'D* RATHER STUDY!

AW, WHO NEEDS THAT WALKIN' BOOKWORM ANYWAY!

IT'LL BE MORE FUN *WITHOUT* HIM!

3

THIS HAPPENED! LOOK AT THIS EDITORIAL! THE PAPER HAS EVERYONE SO STEAMED UP, THEY'LL PROBABLY TOSS YOU IN JAIL IF YOU SHOW YOUR FACE!

BUT WHY? WHAT HAVE THEY GOT AGAINST ME? WHAT HAVE I DONE?

SPIDER-MAN MENACE

BUT, NOT SATISFIED WITH MERELY WRITING EDITORIALS, J. JONAH JAMESON, PUBLISHER OF THE POWERFUL "DAILY BUGLE" DELIVERS LECTURES ALL OVER TOWN...

WE CANNOT ALLOW THAT MASKED MENACE TO TAKE THE LAW INTO HIS OWN HANDS! HE IS A BAD INFLUENCE ON OUR YOUNGSTERS!

CHILDREN MAY TRY TO IMITATE HIS FANTASTIC FEATS!

THINK WHAT WOULD HAPPEN IF THEY MAKE A HERO OUT OF THIS LAWLESS, INHUMAN MONSTER! WE MUST NOT PERMIT IT!

"I SAY THAT SPIDER-MAN MUST BE OUTLAWED! THERE IS NO PLACE FOR SUCH A DANGEROUS CREATURE IN OUR FAIR CITY!"

THE YOUTH OF THIS NATION MUST LEARN TO RESPECT REAL HEROES -- MEN SUCH AS MY SON, JOHN JAMESON, THE TEST PILOT! NOT SELFISH FREAKS SUCH AS SPIDER-MAN -- A MASKED MENACE WHO REFUSES TO EVEN LET US KNOW HIS TRUE IDENTITY!

I DON'T GET IT! HOW DO OTHER SUPERHUMAN GUYS, LIKE THE FANTASTIC FOUR AND THE ANT MAN, GET AWAY WITH IT?? NOBODY BOTHERS THEM! AND THEY ALWAYS SEEM TO MAKE ENOUGH DOUGH!

BAH! I DON'T EVEN BELIEVE THAT THERE IS A SPIDER-MAN! IT'S ALL A PUBLICITY STUNT!

DAILY BUGLE
SPIDER-MAN MENACE
SPIDER-MAN MENACE
SPIDER-MAN MENACE

WELL, IF I CAN'T MAKE A LIVING AS SPIDER-MAN, THE ONLY *OTHER* THING TO DO IS FIND A PART-TIME JOB! I'LL TAKE A LOOK THRU THE WANT ADS...

BUT AGAIN PETER PARKER MEETS WITH FRUSTRATION...

SORRY, SONNY! I AIN'T LOOKIN' FOR A SCHOOL KID! THE JOB I ADVERTISED IS FOR A *MAN!*

BUT...

EXTRA! JOHN JAMESON ABOUT TO ORBIT EARTH IN ROCKET...

SAY -- THAT LOOKS LIKE -- IT *IS!* IT'S AUNT MAY! I WONDER WHERE SHE'S GOING?

OH, *NO!* SHE'S PAWNING HER JEWELRY!

SHE MUST BE *DESPERATE* FOR MONEY! BUT SHE DOESN'T WANT ME TO KNOW! SHE DOESN'T WANT TO WORRY ME!

FOR ME! SHE'S DOING IT ALL FOR ME! AND THERE'S NO WAY I CAN REPAY HER! NO WAY I CAN HELP HER! I CAN'T EVEN FIND A *JOB!*

EXTRA! JOHN JAMESON, SON OF THE PUBLISHER OF THE "DAILY BUGLE" ABOUT TO ORBIT EARTH! *EXTRA!*

IT'S ALL *HIS* FAULT! BECAUSE OF *HIM*, I CAN'T PERFORM IN PUBLIC AS THE SPIDER-MAN!

BUT I CAN'T GIVE UP! I'VE GOT TO EARN SOME MONEY -- SOMEHOW!

I CAN'T LET AUNT MAY DOWN! EVEN IF IT MEANS THE SPIDER-MAN WILL AGAIN STALK THE CITY BY NIGHT!

6

BUT THEN, DISASTER STRIKES! A SMALL SECTION OF THE FORWARD GUIDANCE PACKAGE BREAKS LOOSE FROM THE CAPSULE, AND FALLS INTO SPACE...

WITHOUT THIS ESSENTIAL GUIDANCE UNIT, THE CAPSULE GOES INTO AN ERRATIC ORBIT, COMPLETELY OUT OF CONTROL!

SOMETHING'S WRONG! I CAN'T CONTROL HER!

THIS FLASHING RED LIGHT! IT CAN MEAN ONLY ONE THING! I'VE LOST THE HEART OF THE GUIDANCE DEVICE! THERE IS NO WAY TO DIRECT THE CAPSULE NOW!

MEANWHILE, MILES AWAY...

WHAT IS IT? WHAT WENT WRONG?

CAPSULE IS OUT OF CONTROL, SIR! COMPONENT 24-3B HAS BROKEN LOOSE! CONDITION RED!

WHAT'S THAT?? WITHOUT THE MISSING PART HE WILL CONTINUE TO GO INTO LOWER AND LOWER ORBIT UNTIL HE CRASHES TO EARTH!

GENTLEMEN, WE HAVEN'T MUCH TIME! WE MUST FIND SOME WAY TO SAVE JOHN JAMESON'S LIFE, EVEN THOUGH THE CAPSULE IS DOOMED!

ACTING WITH DESPERATE SPEED, THE SPACE TECHNICIANS ATTEMPT TO DROP A STEEL NET TO CATCH THE CAPSULE, BUT WITH NO SUCCESS!

A COMPLETE MISS! WE'VE GOT TO FIND A BETTER WAY!

WHILE, UNSUSPECTED BY ALL, A BETTER WAY DOES EXIST! IN THE FORM OF PETER PARKER, WHO HAS OBSERVED THE ENTIRE DRAMATIC EVENT...

THERE'S ONLY ONE PERSON WHO CAN SAVE JOHN JAMESON...

8

11

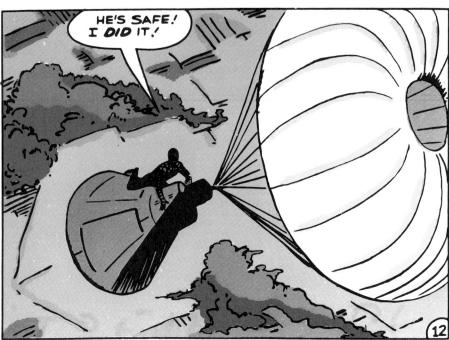

IT WAS ALL A PLOT BY SPIDER-MAN TO STEAL THE SPOTLIGHT FROM MY SON! I ACCUSE SPIDER-MAN *HIM-SELF* OF SABOTAGING THE CAPSULE SO THAT THE GUIDANCE UNIT WOULD FALL OFF!

SPIDER-MAN UNLAWFULLY BROKE INTO A MILITARY BASE AND COMMAN-DEERED A PLANE BY FORCE!

THEN, BY MEANS OF A GRAND-STAND PLAY, HE TRIED TO MAKE A HERO OF HIMSELF, BUT HE CAUSED AN IMPORTANT MISSILE TEST TO FAIL AND SET OUR SPACE PROGRAM BACK BY MANY WEEKS! I REPEAT--SPIDER-MAN IS A *MENACE* TO AMERICA!

UNFORTUNATELY, IF SOMETHING IS SHOUTED LOUD ENOUGH, THERE ARE ALWAYS THOSE WHO WILL *BELIEVE* IT...

THEY FEAR ME MORE THAN *EVER* NOW!

SPIDER-MAN OUGHTTA BE RUN OUT OF THE COUNTRY!

AND HOW!

AND, FINALLY--UNDER PRESSURE OF THE ANGRY NEWSPAPERMAN'S CONTINUAL BARRAGE...

WANTED

CAUTION: HE IS DANGER-OUS

REPORT HIM TO NEAREST F.B.I. OFFICE

SPIDER-MAN

REWARD FOR HIS CAPTURE

OH DEAR, I CERTAINLY HOPE THEY FIND THAT HORRIBLE SPIDER-MAN AND LOCK HIM UP BEFORE HE CAN DO ANY HARM!

WHAT DO I DO *NOW*? HOW CAN I PROVE I'M *NOT* DANGEROUS? HOW CAN I CONVINCE PEOPLE THAT I WASN'T RESPON-SIBLE FOR THE FAILURE OF THAT CAPSULE?

EVERYTHING I DO AS SPIDER-MAN SEEMS TO TURN OUT WRONG! WHAT GOOD IS MY FANTASTIC POWER IF I *CANNOT* USE IT??

OR, MUST I BE FORCED TO BECOME WHAT THEY ACCUSE ME OF BEING?? MUST I *REALLY* BECOME A MENACE? PERHAPS-- THAT IS THE ONLY COURSE LEFT FOR ME!

AND SO, A LONELY BOY SITS AND BROODS, WITH THE FATE OF SOCIETY AT STAKE! WHAT WILL HIS DE-CISION BE? WHAT WILL SPIDER-MAN DO NEXT?? ONLY TIME WILL TELL!

The END

WE KNOW HIM AS PETER PARKER ...BUT THE WORLD KNOWS HIM ONLY AS *SPIDER-MAN!*

SAY! WHY DIDN'T I THINK OF IT *BEFORE? THERE'S* THE WAY I CAN MAKE SOME MONEY-- BY JOINING THE *FANTASTIC FOUR!*

THEY'LL PROBABLY *JUMP* AT THE CHANCE TO HAVE A TEEN-AGER WITH SUPER POWERS WORKING WITH THEM! IT'LL BE A *NATURAL!*

HERE'S THEIR PRIVATE ELEVATOR, BUT THE BLAMED THING ISN'T WORKING!

UH OH-- I FORGOT! IT CAN ONLY BE OPERATED BY ONE OF THE *FOUR,* USING A SPECIAL ELECTRONIC BEAM!

WELL, THAT WON'T STOP *SPIDER-MAN!* FORCING A COUPLE OF LOCKED DOORS OPEN IS MERE CHILD'S PLAY FOR-- *HECK!* I DIDN'T FIGURE THE *ELEVATOR* WOULD BE ABOVE ME! NO ROOM TO CLIMB PAST IT!

MINUTES LATER, PETER PARKER REACHES THE ROOF OF AN ADJOINING BUILDING...

WELL, THERE'S MORE THAN *ONE* WAY TO SKIN A CAT! I SHOULD'VE THOUGHT OF THIS RIGHT AWAY!

THEY'LL PROBABLY BE *TWICE* AS IMPRESSED WHEN THEY SEE HOW EASILY I GET INTO THEIR PRIVATE SKYSCRAPER HEADQUARTERS!

HERE GOES NOTHING!

MEANWHILE, DOWN BELOW...

IT'S THE *SPIDER-MAN!* WHAT A BONUS I'LL GET FOR *THIS* SHOT!

HE'S HEAD-ING FOR THE *FANTASTIC FOUR'S* HEAD-QUARTERS!

HE BALANCES HIMSELF ON THAT STRAND OF WEB LIKE A HUMAN SPIDER!

AT THAT MOMENT, AN *ALARM* RINGS IN THE READY ROOM OF THE *FANTASTIC FOUR...*

THE *ALARM!* SOMEONE IS TRYING TO SNEAK IN!

HE MUST BE SOME KINDA *NUT* TO THINK HE CAN TAKE *US* BY SURPRISE!

BRIN-N-NG!

TOO BAD HE LEFT SO SUDDENLY! PERHAPS WE COULD HAVE *HELPED* HIM!

AWW! WE'VE GOT *ENOUGH* PROBLEM KIDS TO WORRY ABOUT NOW!

SOMEHOW, I HAVE A FEELING WE'LL BE HEARING *MORE* FROM THAT YOUNG MAN IN THE FUTURE!

AND NOW OUR SCENE SHIFTS TO A DEFENSE INSTALLATION AT THE EDGE OF TOWN...

WITH MY MULTI-POCKET DISGUISE VEST, IT WILL BE AN EASY MATTER FOR *THE CHAMELEON* TO BECOME *YOU*, FRIEND JANITOR!

MINUTES LATER...

SO FAR SO GOOD! DISGUISED AS THE JANITOR, IT WAS EASY TO GAIN ACCESS TO THIS RESTRICTED AREA!

AND NOW, ANOTHER FAST CHANGE AND I WILL TAKE THE THE IDENTITY OF PROFESSOR NEWTON!

HAH! NOTHING CAN STOP *THE CHAMELEON!* WITH THE RIGHT DISGUISE, I CAN STEAL ANYTHING FROM ANYWHERE, UNCHALLENGED!

THAT NIGHT AT *THE CHAMELEON'S* HIDEOUT...

THE IRON CURTAIN COUNTRIES WILL PAY A FORTUNE FOR THESE PLANS!

HMM... A T.V. NEWS BULLETIN...

THE ENTIRE CITY IS WONDERING WHY *SPIDER-MAN* VISITED THE *FANTASTIC FOUR* TODAY! "NO COMMENT" SAYS THE FF!

RUMORS ARE FLYING ALL OVER NEW YORK! UNOFFICIAL SOURCES CLAIM *SPIDER-MAN* IS BEING CONSIDERED FOR *MEMBERSHIP* IN THE *FF!* "NONSENSE!" CLAIMS THE POLICE COMMISSIONER!

HMM... I THINK *SPIDER-MAN'S* VISIT IS OF INTEREST TO *THE CHAMELEON*, TOO!

YES, INDEED-- *VERY* INTERESTING!

ILY GLOBE

LATEST ON SPIDER-MAN

GRAND JURY REQUESTS IMMEDIATE PROBE.

The F.B.I. has been alerted for possible action

THERE IS ONLY *ONE* REASON *SPIDER-MAN* WOULD WANT TO JOIN THE *FANTASTIC FOUR!* BEING SOUGHT BY THE POLICE, THERE IS NO WAY FOR HIM TO EARN A LEGITIMATE LIVING! HE MUST BE DESPERATE FOR MONEY! AND THIS IS WHERE *I* COME IN!

SPIDER-MAN WILL MAKE A PERFECT *FALL GUY*-- FOR ME! WHEN I STEAL THE SECOND HALF OF THESE MISSILE DEFENSE PLANS, I'LL HAVE HIM PUT THE POLICE OFF MY TRAIL!

5

SPIDER-MAN HAS THE POWERS AND INSTINCTS OF A SPIDER! SO I WILL SEND HIM A MESSAGE THAT ONLY HIS SPIDER SENSES WILL BE ABLE TO PICK UP!

CALLING SPIDER-MAN! MEET ME ON ROOF OF LARK BUILDING AT TEN TONIGHT! IT WILL BE VERY PROFITABLE FOR YOU!

AND MILES AWAY, AT A NEIGHBORHOOD MUSEUM, WHERE PETER PARKER IS STUDYING THE SPIDER EXHIBIT...

SOMEONE IS TRYING TO CONTACT SPIDER-MAN! I CAN SENSE THE FREQUENCY WAVES! BUT WHO--?

WELL, NO MATTER WHO IT IS, I CAN'T AFFORD TO PASS UP A CHANCE FOR PROFIT! I'LL JUST LEAVE MY CLOTHES UP HERE, AND THEN...

A FEW MINUTES BEFORE TEN P.M....

ALMOST TIME FOR ME TO TAKE OVER THE ELEVATOR NIGHT SHIFT!

YES, IT IS TIME! BUT NOT FOR YOU-- FOR THE CHAMELEON!

AFTER BINDING AND GAGGING THE REAL ELEVATOR OPERATOR, THE BOGUS ONE BRAZENLY TAKES HIS PLACE!

I'LL RELIEVE YOU NOW!

IT'S ABOUT TIME! I'M BUSHED!

THEN, ONCE INSIDE THE ELEVATOR...

SO FAR, MY TIME-TABLE IS RUNNING RIGHT TO THE SPLIT-SECOND! NOW TO CHANGE TO MY SPIDER-MAN GUISE!

AND FINALLY...

SPIDER-MAN! H-HOW DID YOU GET IN? W-WHAT DO YOU WANT?

THOSE MISSILE DEFENSE PLANS WHICH YOU'RE HOLDING!

I CAN'T BELIEVE IT! YOU-- A TRAITOR! WAIT--

MY WEB WILL KEEP YOU A PRISONER UNTIL I CAN ESCAPE!

THIS ARTIFICIAL WEB ISN'T AS STRONG AS SPIDER-MAN'S REAL ONE, BUT NO ONE'LL NOTICE THE DIFFERENCE!

6

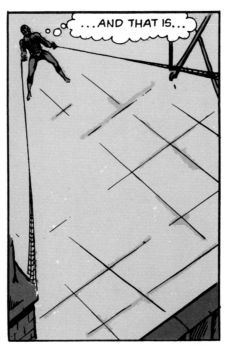

I'VE GOT TO REACH THAT EXIT BEFORE *HE* DOES! THIS IS THE *FASTEST* WAY!

THAT FIGURE-- LEAVING THE OTHERS-- IT'S *HIM!*

BUT, AS THE LIGHTS GO ON AGAIN, *THE CHAMELEON* RESORTS TO ONE, LAST, DESPERATE RUSE...

HELP! GRAB HIM! IT'S *THE CHAMELEON,* DISGUISED AS *SPIDER-MAN* AGAIN!

WHA--?

OH, *NO,* YOU DON'T! YOU'RE NOT GONNA FOOL US THAT WAY A *SECOND* TIME!

WAIT!... HE'S *LYING!* I AM SPIDER-MAN!

IT *WORKED!* NOW TO SLIP AWAY!

IN A FIT OF WHITE-HOT FURY, THE POWERFUL *SPIDER-MAN* WRENCHES FREE OF THE STARTLED OFFICERS' GRASP, AND...

LOOK AT HIM GO UP THAT WALL! HE *WAS* THE *REAL* SPIDER-MAN!

EVERY TIME I TRY TO HELP, I GET INTO *WORSE* TROUBLE! WELL, THEY CAN CATCH THAT SPY *THEMSELVES* NOW!

AND WITHIN MINUTES, CATCH HIM THEY *DO* ...

HERE HE *IS,* CAPTAIN! I SPOTTED HIM BY HIS TORN UNIFORM-- I COULD SEE HIS OTHER DISGUISE BENEATH IT!

BLAST IT! I MUST HAVE RIPPED IT IN MY SCUFFLE WITH *SPIDER-MAN!*

AND, AS *THE CHAMELEON* IS LED AWAY, A LONE FIGURE LOSES HIMSELF IN THE SHADOWS OF THE SILENT NIGHT...

NOTHING TURNS OUT RIGHT...;*SOB*:...I WISH I HAD NEVER *GOTTEN* MY SUPER POWERS!

LATER, AS THE LATE EDITIONS COME OUT, FOUR FAMOUS FIGURES PONDER THE CASE OF THE AMAZING *SPIDER-MAN!*

REED, HE'S SO POWERFUL, AND SO CONFUSED! WHAT IF *SPIDER-MAN* EVER TURNS HIS SUPER POWERS *AGAINST* THE LAW?

YEAH! IF A *TEEN-AGER* CAN BE SO BLAMED STRONG, HOW STRONG'LL HE BE WHEN HE GETS *OLDER?*

AW, WE WON'T EVER HAFTA WORRY ABOUT *HIM!*

WON'T WE, JOHNNY? I WONDER...

AND THE WHOLE *WORLD* WILL HAVE TO WONDER-- UNTIL OUR NEXT GREAT ISSUE! *DON'T MISS IT!!*

The END

⑩

SECRETS of SPIDER-MAN'S WEB

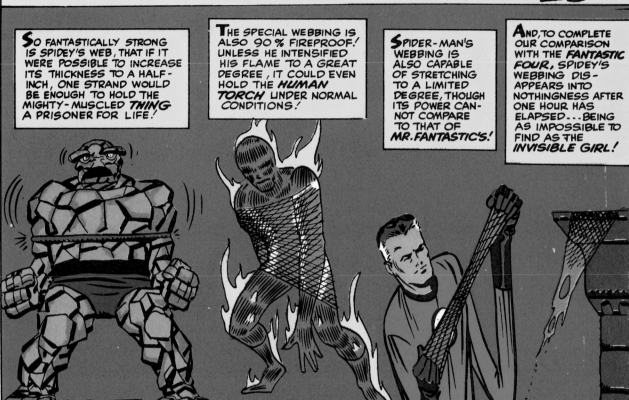

So FANTASTICALLY STRONG IS SPIDEY'S WEB, THAT IF IT WERE POSSIBLE TO INCREASE ITS THICKNESS TO A HALF-INCH, ONE STRAND WOULD BE ENOUGH TO HOLD THE MIGHTY-MUSCLED *THING* A PRISONER FOR LIFE!

THE SPECIAL WEBBING IS ALSO 90% FIREPROOF! UNLESS HE INTENSIFIED HIS FLAME TO A GREAT DEGREE, IT COULD EVEN HOLD THE *HUMAN TORCH* UNDER NORMAL CONDITIONS!

SPIDER-MAN'S WEBBING IS ALSO CAPABLE OF STRETCHING TO A LIMITED DEGREE, THOUGH ITS POWER CAN-NOT COMPARE TO THAT OF *MR. FANTASTIC'S!*

AND, TO COMPLETE OUR COMPARISON WITH THE *FANTASTIC FOUR*, SPIDEY'S WEBBING DIS-APPEARS INTO NOTHINGNESS AFTER ONE HOUR HAS ELAPSED...BEING AS IMPOSSIBLE TO FIND AS THE *INVISIBLE GIRL!*

HAVING DEVOTED MANY LONG HOURS OF PRACTICE TO THE OPERATION OF HIS WEB, THE TERRIFIC TEEN-AGER CAN NOW USE IT IN MANY DIFFERENT WAYS...

AS A SHIELD...

A PARACHUTE...

A SAFETY NET...

A BARRIER...

AS SKIIS...

AS A RAFT...

AS A CLUB...

A BALL

OR PLAIN, SIMPLE STICKY GLUE!

ALONE IN THE DESERT STANDS THE MOST AWESOME WEAPON EVER CREATED BY MAN--*THE INCREDIBLE G-BOMB!*

MILES AWAY, BEHIND SOLID CONCRETE BUNKERS, A NERVOUS SCIENTIFIC TASK FORCE WAITS FOR THE GAMMA-BOMB'S FIRST AWESOME TEST FIRING!

AND NONE IS MORE TENSE, MORE WORRIED, THAN DR. BRUCE BANNER, THE MAN WHOSE GENIUS CREATED THE G-BOMB!

A FEW SECONDS MORE AND WE'LL KNOW WHETHER WE HAVE SUCCEEDED OR NOT!

I WAS AGAINST IT FROM THE START, BANNER, AND I STILL AM! IT IS *TOO DANGEROUS!*

I *STILL* SAY YOU SHOULD HAVE CONFIDED IN US, YOUR FELLOW SCIENTISTS! YOU SHOULD HAVE TOLD US THE SECRET OF THE GAMMA RAY...

QUIET, IGOR! HERE COMES GENERAL ROSS!

WHY THE *DELAY,* BANNER? WHAT ARE YOU *WAITING* FOR?

MY MEN HAVE BEEN STATIONED HERE FOR WEEKS, WASTING TIME BECAUSE OF YOUR INFERNAL DELAYS! ARE YOU GOING TO TEST THAT BLAMED BOMB OR *NOT?*

OF COURSE, GENERAL! IT'S JUST THAT I MUST BE SURE EVERY PRECAUTION HAS BEEN TAKEN! WE ARE TAMPERING WITH POWERFUL FORCES!

POWERFUL FORCES! *BAH!!* A BOMB IS A BOMB! THE TROUBLE WITH *YOU* IS YOU'RE A *MILKSOP!* YOU'VE GOT NO *GUTS!*

THEY SHOULD HAVE PUT *ME* IN CHARGE OF THIS TEST! BY THUNDER, IT WOULD HAVE BEEN *DONE* BY NOW!

OH DADDY, DON'T BE SO UNFAIR! DR. BRUCE BANNER IS ONE OF OUR MOST FAMOUS SCIENTISTS! I'M *SURE* HE KNOWS WHAT HE'S DOING!

YOU KEEP OUT OF THIS, BETTY! THIS IS *MAN TALK!*

DON'T MIND DAD, DR. BANNER! EVER SINCE HE WAS NICKNAMED "THUNDERBOLT" ROSS, HE'S TRIED TO LIVE UP TO IT!

HRMMPHH!

THANK YOU, MISS ROSS!

2

PART 2

THE HULK STRIKES!

LIKE A SILENT DREADNAUGHT, THE HULKING THING THAT WAS ONCE BRUCE BANNER CROUCHES IN THE SHADOWS, AS THE PURSUING TROOPS RUSH BY...

MUSTN'T LET THEM FIND ME...

FAN OUT, MEN! WE'VE GOT TO FIND THAT--THAT *HULK*!!

LOOK SHARP THERE! DON'T LET THE HULK GET HIS HANDS ON YOU!

AND THUS, A *NAME* IS GIVEN TO BRUCE BANNER'S OTHER SELF, A NAME WHICH IS DESTINED TO BECOME-- IMMORTAL!

WHILE, BACK AT THE BASE HOSPITAL...

IT'S *IMPOSSIBLE!* NOTHING HUMAN COULD HAVE SMASHED A TWO FOOT THICK CONCRETE *WALL!*

BUT HE *DID!* THE HULK *DID* IT!

BRUCE BANNER AND THE BOY! WHAT BECAME OF *THEM?* COULD THE HULK HAVE--??

BUT WHO COULD EVER GUESS THE INCREDIBLE TRUTH? WHO COULD SUSPECT THAT BRUCE BANNER *IS*... THE HULK!!!

WH-WHERE IS HE *HEADED* FOR?

HAVE TO KEEP MOVING...

...HAVE TO REACH HOME! FORMULA INSIDE HOME! MUST GET FORMULA!!

DRIVEN BY SHEER INSTINCT, THE PART OF THE HULK WHICH IS STILL BRUCE BANNER HEADS FOR A SMALL COTTAGE, SMASHING ALL OBSTACLES IN HIS PATH!

MOVING WITH UNBELIEVABLE STEALTH FOR ONE SO PONDEROUS, HE STORMS CLOSER AND CLOSER TO HIS DESTINATION ...

UNTIL, AT LAST, A DIM MEMORY FROM THE BRAIN OF BRUCE BANNER TELLS HIM ...

THE THIRD CABIN! THAT IS WHERE I MUST GO!

8

9

10

I -- I SEEM TO *REMEMBER* NOW! IT WAS THE BOMB! *THE GAMMA RAYS!* THEY TURNED ME INTO -- *THIS* -- WHEN DARKNESS FELL!

IT WOULD HAVE HAPPENED TO *ME* IF YOU HADN'T SAVED ME! THAT'S WHY I'M STAYIN' *WITH* YOU!

FOOL! I AM *GLAD* IT HAPPENED!! I'D RATHER BE *ME*, THAN THAT PUNY WEAKLING IN THE PICTURE!

I DON'T WANT YOU WITH ME! I DON'T NEED YOU! I DON'T NEED *ANYBODY!* WITH MY STRENGTH -- MY POWER -- THE *WORLD* IS MINE!

AS FOR *YOU* -- YOU ARE THE ONLY ONE WHO KNOWS WHO I REALLY *AM!*

WHA-- WHAT DO YOU *MEAN?*

BUT, AT THAT VERY INSTANT, THE FIRST RAYS OF *DAWN* APPEAR! AND WITH THEM--

MY HEAD!!

MY BRAIN -- IT'S ON FIRE!

WHAT IS *HAPPENING* TO ME? I-- I'M *CHANGING!!*

CHANGING---

IT--IT FEELS AS THOUGH A *VEIL* HAS LIFTED -- I CAN *THINK* AGAIN!

IT'S *OVER!* THE NIGHTMARE IS *OVER!*

GOSH! YOU-- YOU'RE DOCTOR BRUCE BANNER AGAIN!

BUT, ALAS, THE NIGHTMARE OF BRUCE BANNER IS *NOT* YET OVER! IT MAY *NEVER* BE OVER AGAIN!

OPEN UP IN THERE!

THIS IS THE POLICE!

11

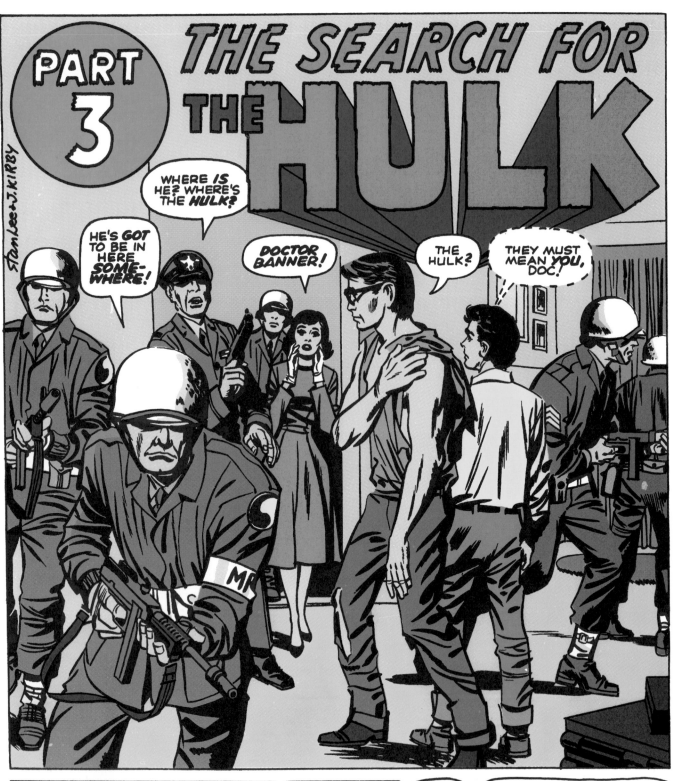

WHAT HAPPENED TO *YOU*, DOCTOR BANNER? WHY DID YOU LEAVE THE HOSPITAL? HOW DID YOU GET THAT SHOULDER WOUND?

HOW DO WE KNOW *YOU'RE* NOT MIXED UP IN THIS?

ARE YOU *KIDDIN'*?! WHAT DO YOU THINK HE *IS*... THE *HULK*?!

CAPTAIN, WE WERE IN THE JEEP WHICH *HIT* THE HULK! WE GOT A GOOD LOOK AT HIM!

HE WAS *NOTHING* LIKE DR. BANNER!

HE WAS HUGE, POWERFUL! IN FACT, I WOULDN'T BE SURPRISED IF HE WAS A GIANT GORILLA THAT ESCAPED FROM SOME ZOO!

NO, HE WAS MORE LIKE A BIG BEAR, DRESSED IN TATTERS! PROBABLY ESCAPED FROM A CIRCUS SOMEWHERE!

PERSONALLY, I THINK YOU JOKERS WERE *SEEIN'* THINGS! HE WAS JUST A LITTLE CUB SCOUT ON PATROL!

IT'S FORTUNATE THAT IGOR DID NOT GET YOUR GAMMA BOMB FORMULA! I'LL TAKE IT FOR SAFE-KEEPING!

MINUTES LATER, AFTER THE TROOPS HAVE LEFT TO CONTINUE THEIR VAIN SEARCH FOR THE HULK...

DOCTOR BANNER, I RETURNED TO APOLOGIZE FOR MY FATHER'S REMARKS TO YOU! BUT I NEVER EXPECTED TO FIND...

TO FIND ME IN THE MIDDLE OF A SEARCH FOR A-- MONSTER?

NEITHER DID *I*! NEITHER =SOB= DID I!

YOU'RE ILL! YOU NEED MEDICAL CARE!

NO HE DOESN'T LADY! HE JUST NEEDS A LITTLE PEACE AND QUIET, THAT'S ALL!

13

MISS ROSS, FORGIVE ME! I'VE--BEEN UNDER A TERRIBLE STRAIN! RICK WILL SHOW YOU TO THE DOOR!

SURE, DOC! YOU JUST TAKE IT EASY!

VERY WELL... I'LL GO! BUT, IF YOU SHOULD *NEED* ME--

MISS ROSS--BETTY-- I'LL CALL YOU LATER-- AFTER I'VE HAD A CHANCE TO PULL MYSELF TOGETHER!

OH, IT'S *BETTY* NOW! BAH! HOW REVOLTIN!

PLEASE DO... BRUCE! I FEEL YOU'RE IN SOME GREAT TROUBLE, AND--I WANT TO HELP!

BOY! I THOUGHT THEY'D NEVER LEAVE! NOW WE CAN *TALK!*

WHAT DID IT *FEEL* LIKE, DOC, BEIN THE HULK? I'LL BET IT WAS *A GAS!*

SAY! WHAT'S WRONG? IT'S ALL *OVER* NOW, ISN'T IT?

OVER? NO, RICK, IT *ISN'T* OVER! IT'S JUST... *BEGINNING!*

REMEMBER, I BECAME THE HULK WHEN NIGHT FELL, AND RETURNED TO MY NORMAL SELF AT DAY-BREAK! BUT DAY DOESN'T LAST FOREVER! IT WILL SOON BE *NIGHT* AGAIN...

...AND WHEN THE SUN SETS, HOW DO I KNOW I WON'T CHANGE *ONCE MORE?* HOW DO I KNOW I WON'T *KEEP* CHANGING...

...INTO THAT BRUTAL, BESTIAL MOCKERY OF A HUMAN-- THAT CREATURE WHICH FEARS NOTHING--WHICH DESPISES REASON AND WORSHIPS POWER!

SOON, THE SUN WILL SET AGAIN! AND HERE I SIT, HELPLESSLY, FEARING I MAY AGAIN BECOME--*THE HULK!!*

14

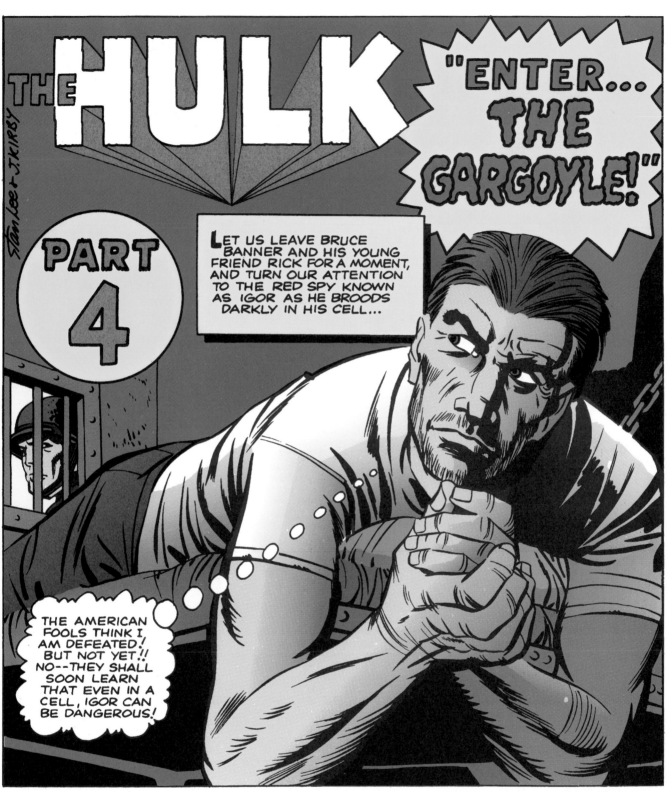

16

BRIEF HOURS LATER, THE VERY LATEST MODEL RED SUB CUTS THRU THE MURKY DEPTHS OF THE SEA...

UNTIL, REACHING A PRE-ARRANGED AREA, IT UN-LEASHES AN EXPERIMENTAL MAN-CARRYING ROCKET!

WHAT'S THAT?? OUR RADAR HAS TRACKED AN UNIDENTIFIED MISSILE HEADING THIS WAY??!

UNLEASH OUR HUNTER MISSILES!

WITHIN SECONDS, AMERICA'S MIGHTY DEFENSE STRUCTURE UNLEASHES ITS FANTASTIC ARSENAL, AND...

THE MISSILE IS DESTROYED! BUT I HAVE LANDED AT MY DESTINATION SAFELY!

AND NOW... IT IS TIME FOR THE GARGOYLE TO MEET... THE HULK!

AND SO, FATE TWISTS THE THREADS OF OUR TALE TIGHTER AND TIGHTER, UNTIL...

WHERE ARE YOU GOING, DOC? IT'LL BE EVENING SOON! SHOULDN'T WE BE AT HOME, WAITING TO SEE--?

NO, RICK! IF I AM DESTINED TO BECOME THAT INHUMAN CREATURE AGAIN, LET IT HAPPEN OUT IN THE OPEN THIS TIME!

IT'S HARD TO BELIEVE, DOC! YOU'RE THE MOST FAMOUS MISSILE EXPERT IN THE WORLD! YOU'RE BRAINY AND CULTURED, AND ALL THAT JAZZ! AND YET...

AND YET, DUE TO THE FORCES UN-LEASHED BY THE GAMMA RAY, I TURN INTO A MARAUDING, SAVAGE BRUTE AT NIGHTFALL!

17

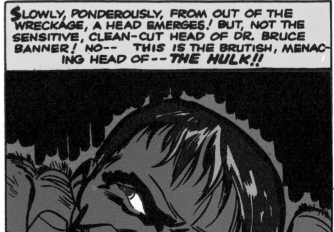

MEANWHILE, JUST A SHORT DISTANCE AWAY, BETTY ROSS IS LOST IN HER OWN DISTURBED MUSINGS...

I CAN'T GET BRUCE BANNER OUT OF MY MIND!!

SOMEHOW, I FEEL HE-- NEEDS ME!

WHAT IS IT, GIRL? YOU'VE SEEMED TROUBLED ALL DAY!

OH, DAD... IF ONLY THINGS WERE AS SIMPLE AS IN YOUR DAY, WHEN A CAVALRY CHARGE, OR A SQUAD OF INFANTRYMEN COULD SOLVE ANYTHING!

BUT TODAY, WITH THE STRANGE, ALMOST SUPERNATURAL FORCES ALL AROUND US, I FEEL AS THOUGH WE'RE ON THE BRINK OF SOME FANTASTIC UNIMAGINABLE ADVENTURE!

HONEY, YOU JUST NEED A LITTLE FRESH AIR!

DAD'S RIGHT! PERHAPS A WALK IN THE CRISP NIGHT AIR WILL CLEAR MY HEAD--WILL DRIVE THE TROUBLED FACE OF BRUCE BANNER FROM MY THOUGHTS!

AND PERHAPS I CAN TELL MYSELF IT WAS ALL A DREAM-- THERE IS NO HULK!

BUT THERE IS A HULK!! AND DON'T YOU EVER FORGET IT!!

OH-- NO!

FAINTED!! BAH! JUST LIKE ALL WEAK, HELPLESS CREATURES!

HULK-- LET GO OF HER!

YOU'VE GOT TO LEAVE HERE! IF YOU'RE FOUND THIS TIME, THEY'LL--

SHUT UP! NOBODY TELLS THE HULK!

YOU ARE WRONG, MONSTER! TURN AROUND! TURN AND FACE--THE GARGOYLE!

19

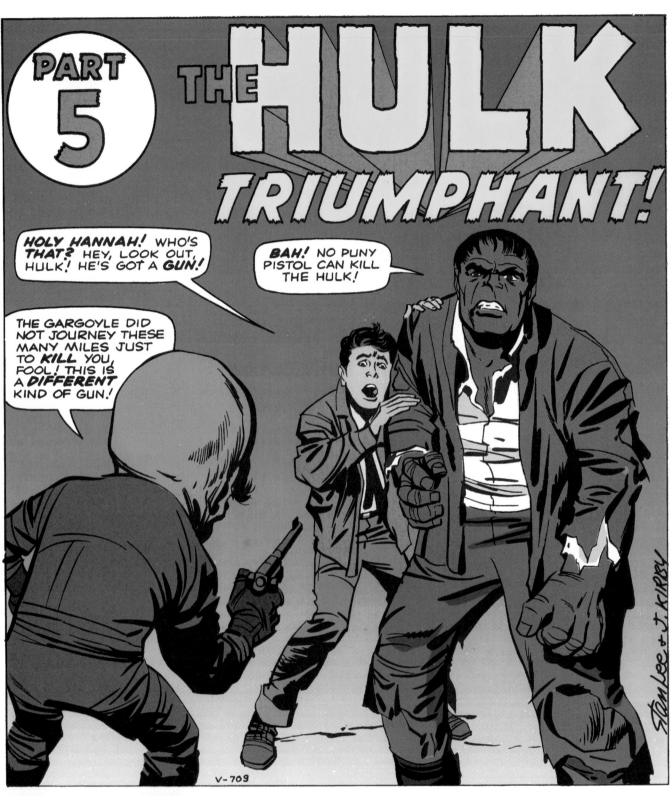

HAH! THE GARGOYLE IS NEVER WRONG! AND THOUGH *YOU* SEEM TOO UNIMPORTANT TO WASTE ANOTHER PELLET ON, I BELIEVE IN TAKING NO CHANCES!

IT IS *DONE!* BOTH OF YOU... RISE, AND FOLLOW ME!

RISE...

FORTUNATELY, IN THE EXCITEMENT OF THE MOMENT, THE GARGOYLE DOES NOT NOTICE THE UNCONSCIOUS GIRL LYING IN THE SHADOWS BEHIND HIS TWO HELPLESS PRISONERS!

HOW EASY IT IS FOR THE GARGOYLE TO BE VICTORIOUS!

AND MOMENTS LATER...

BETTY! BETTY!

DAD... IT-- IT WAS HORRIBLE!

IT WAS *THE HULK!* HE CAME FROM OUT OF THE DARKNESS! HE--HE WAS *TERRIFYING!*

THERE, THERE, MY DEAR! YOU'RE SAFE NOW!

BUT WHERE DID HE *GO?* WHAT DID HE *WANT?* OR--OR DID I *IMAGINE* THE WHOLE THING?

I'LL *FIND* HIM, BETTY! I *SWEAR* TO YOU, MY CHILD, I'LL FIND HIM AND DESTROY HIM!

AND YET, IN SPITE OF EVERYTHING, THERE WAS SOMETHING... SOMETHING *SAD* ABOUT HIM!! ALMOST AS THOUGH HE WAS SEEKING... HELP!

I'LL FIND HIM! IF IT TAKES AN *ETERNITY,* I'LL FIND THAT MONSTER!

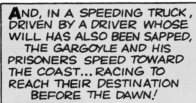

AND, IN A SPEEDING TRUCK, DRIVEN BY A DRIVER WHOSE WILL HAS ALSO BEEN SAPPED, THE GARGOYLE AND HIS PRISONERS SPEED TOWARD THE COAST... RACING TO REACH THEIR DESTINATION BEFORE THE DAWN!

FASTER! *FASTER!*

WHAT A *PRIZE* THE HULK WILL BE.!! WHAT A FANTASTIC SPECIMEN FOR OUR SCIENTISTS TO STUDY! IF WE COULD CREATE AN *ARMY* OF SUCH POWERFUL CREATURES, WE COULD RULE THE EARTH!

21

FINALLY, IN THE EARLY HOURS BEFORE DAYBREAK, THE RENDEZVOUS IS REACHED!

HURRY! ROW FASTER, YOU DOLTS! NOTHING MUST STOP ME NOW!

AND NOTHING *DOES* STOP THE GARGOYLE! FOR, MINUTES LATER...

MADE IT!

AH, WE HAVE REACHED THE EDGE OF SPACE! NOW WE SHALL LEVEL OFF AND GLIDE BE- HIND THE IRON CURTAIN!

BUT THEN, THE FIRST FAINT RAYS OF DAWN TOUCH THE HULK, AS HE SITS IN THE CABIN OF THE PLANE WHICH THE REDS HAVE COPIED FROM OUR OWN AMAZING X-15!

AND, AS DAYLIGHT BATHES HIS BRUTAL FEATURES, ONCE AGAIN A STARTLING, INCREDIBLE *CHANGE* TAKES PLACE!

WHERE ONCE THE MIGHTY *HULK* HAD BEEN, THE LIGHT OF THE SUN NOW REVEALS DR. BRUCE BANNER, AMERICAN SCIENTIST! THE CHANGE IS NOW COMPLETE!

HOURS LATER, AS THE RED SHIP GLIDES TO A LANDING ON COMMUNIST SOIL, THE GARGOYLE RECEIVES A START- LING SURPRISE!

≡WHEW≡ I'M GLAD THE EFFECT OF THAT GUN WORE OFF!

THE HULK!! WHAT HAPPENED TO THE HULK??!

GOT ANY IDEA WHAT THIS JOKER IS *TALKIN'* ABOUT, DOC?

NOT THE SLIGHTEST, RICK!

"DOC"? *WAIT!* I KNOW YOU!! OF COURSE! YOU'RE AMERICA'S FOREMOST ATOMIC SCIENTIST... DR. BRUCE BANNER.!! THAT MEANS YOU... AND THE HULK-- *OH NO!!* IT'S--IT'S TOO *UNBELIEVABLE!*

22

UNDER CLOSE GUARD, THE GARGOYLE RUSHES HIS PRISONERS TO HIS SECRET STRONGHOLD, AND THEN...

YOUR SECRET IS A SECRET NO LONGER, BANNER! I *KNOW* THAT YOU AND THE HULK ARE THE SAME!!

DOC! WHAT DO WE DO *NOW?*

EASY, RICK! IT'S *HIS* PLAY SO FAR!

BUT WHY? WHY WOULD YOU *WANT* TO BE A *MONSTER?* YOU MUST BE *INSANE!* IT--IT'S THE MOST HORRIBLE THING IN THE WORLD TO BE A FREAK-- A GARGOYLE! LIKE *ME!*

DOC! HE'S CRYING!

I'D GIVE *ANYTHING* TO BE NORMAL! *ANYTHING!*

SO WOULD I-- I AM AS HELPLESS AS YOU!

WAIT! *LISTEN* TO ME! I CANNOT *STOP* MYSELF FROM TURNING INTO THE HULK-- BUT *YOUR* CASE IS DIFFERENT!

I'VE *SEEN* CASES LIKE YOURS! I KNOW HOW TO CURE YOU... *BY RADIATION!* BUT ALTHOUGH YOUR FEATURES WOULD BECOME NORMAL, YOUR BRAIN WOULD SUFFER! YOU WOULD NO LONGER BE A BRILLIANT SCIENTIST!

DOC! YOU AIN'T GONNA *HELP* THAT CREEP, ARE YOU??!

QUIET, RICK!

NO MATTER *WHAT* HAPPENS TO ME... EVEN IF I *DIE*... SO LONG AS I COULD DIE AS-- *A MAN!*

THEN, AT A COMMAND FROM THE GARGOYLE, ALL IS MADE READY...

NOW!

AND, WHERE A *GARGOYLE* HAD BEEN LYING...

DOC! IT'S WORKING!

...*A MAN* ARISES!

YOU *DID* IT!

YOU DID IT!

IGNORING THE TWO OTHERS IN THE SILENT LAB, THE LONE FIGURE WALKS TO A PORTRAIT ON THE WALL, AND THEN, IN QUIVERING TONES, HE SPEAKS...

IT WAS BECAUSE OF *YOU* THAT I BECAME WHAT I WAS! BECAUSE I WORKED ON YOUR SECRET BOMB TESTS!

BUT IT TOOK AN *AMERICAN* TO CURE ME! AND NOW--NOW THAT I AM NO LONGER A GARGOYLE, I CAN *DEFY* YOU, AND ALL YOU STAND FOR, LIKE A *MAN!*

23

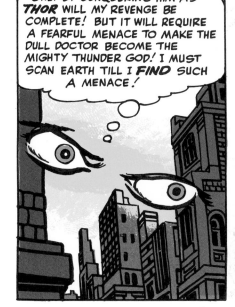

2.

ALTHOUGH THERE IS NO EVIL IN HIS HEART, MANKIND *FEARS* HIM BECAUSE OF HIS AWESOME STRENGTH! *HE* SHALL BE THE PERFECT FOIL FOR ME!

BUT, WHAT DIABOLICAL SCHEME SHALL I EMPLOY? AH, I HAVE IT! THAT *RAILROAD TRESTLE!*

ALL I NEED DO IS PROJECT A MENTAL IMAGE UPON THE TRACKS, WHERE THE *HULK* WILL SEE IT!

THERE, IT IS DONE! THE WITLESS MORTAL WILL THINK HE SEES A REAL BUNDLE OF TNT, ABOUT TO DESTROY THE TRESTLE JUST AS THE TRAIN IS APPROACHING!

PERFECT! HE *SEES* IT! AND NOW, NOT DREAMING IT IS ONLY A NON-EXISTENT IMAGE, HE LEAPS DOWN TO SNUFF IT OUT BEFORE IT CAN EXPLODE!

BUT THERE IS *NO* TNT, AND SO, REACHING FOR SOMETHING THAT IS NOT THERE, HE MISCALCULATES THE FORCE OF HIS PLUNGE, CRASHING INTO THE TRESTLE, AND *SHATTERING* IT!

CHARLIE! *STOP THE TRAIN!* SOMETHING SMASHED THE TRESTLE UP AHEAD! WE'LL *CRASH!*

IMPOSSIBLE!! WE'RE GOING TOO FAST! WE'LL *NEVER* STOP IN TIME!

HAH! IT WORKED JUST AS I PLANNED! WHEN THE TRAIN CRASHES, THE *HULK* WILL BE BLAMED! HE WILL BECOME THE MOST WANTED MAN ON EARTH! DR. BLAKE IS CERTAIN TO BECOME *THOR* TO JOIN IN THE HUNT... LITTLE DREAMING THAT THAT IS JUST WHAT *LOKI* WANTS! BUT, *WAIT!* WHY IS THE *HULK* CARRYING THAT HUGE BOULDER?

HE HAS PLACED IT UNDER THE TRACKS!...IS USING IT AS A SUPPORT, TO STAND ON! THE *FOOL!* WHAT GOOD WILL *THAT* DO? THE TRAIN IS ALMOST UPON HIM!

3.

LOOK! THAT HEAD JUTTING THROUGH THE TRACKS!

IT'S THE HULK! HE DID THIS! HE'S TRYING TO KILL US ALL! I--I CAN'T STOP IN TIME!

BUT, USING THE ALMOST LIMITLESS STRENGTH OF HIS INCREDIBLE BODY, THE **HULK** BENDS BELOW THE TRACKS, SUPPORTING THEM WITH HIS MASSIVE BACK, AS THE TRAIN PASSES SAFELY BY...

BUT THEN...

ALL SAFE! ..CAN'T HOLD ANY LONGER...

WHOOSH!

CRASH!

HE SAVED THE TRAIN, BUT ONLY **I** KNOW THAT! THE HUMANS WILL STILL THINK HE TRIED TO SLAY THEM ...THE HUNT WILL BE ON! AND **THOR** WILL LIVE AGAIN!....ALL BECAUSE OF **LOKI**, THE MASTER SCHEMER!

HOURS LATER, AS **LOKI** PREDICTED...

BETTER LOCK YOUR DOORS, BOYS! THE **HULK'S** ON THE RAMPAGE AGAIN!

A LOT OF GOOD LOCKING A DOOR WILL DO AGAINST **THAT** GORILLA!

HULK IN ATTACK ON TRAIN!

NATION SHOCKED! ARMY TO MOBILIZE!

THEN, THE ONE LIVING BEING WHO KNOWS THE TRUTH ABOUT THE **HULK** READS THE REPORT IN AMAZEMENT!

IT **CAN'T** BE! HE'D **NEVER** DO A THING LIKE THAT!..NO MATTER **WHAT!!**

OR..OR **WOULD** HE?

CITY NEWS TRAIN ENGINEER IDENTIFIES HULK AS WOULD-BE WRECKER!

HULK IN ATT ON TRA

WITHIN MINUTES, **RICK JONES** SUMMONS MEMBERS OF HIS NEWLY FORMED **TEEN BRIGADE,*** A GROUP OF YOUTHFUL RADIO HAM ENTHUSIASTS...

IF THE **HULK** IS INNOCENT, HE NEEDS HELP, FAST! AND IF HE'S GUILTY, IT'LL TAKE MORE THAN THE **ARMY** TO STOP 'IM!

WE'VE GOTTA CONTACT SOMEONE WITH EQUAL POWERS...LIKE THE **FANTASTIC FOUR!**

*TEEN BRIGADE FORMED IN ISSUE OF **HULK** #6.

DON'T JUST SIT THERE, FELLA! START SENDING! USE THE **FF'S** SPECIAL WAVELENGTH! TELL 'EM TO CONTACT ME, **PRONTO,** BEFORE ANY INNOCENT JOKERS GET HURT REAL BAD!

YOU HEARD THE MAN, WILLIE! NOW **MOVE!**

AND SO, SECONDS LATER, A FRANTIC MESSAGE IS BEAMED FROM THE HEADQUARTERS OF THE **TEEN BRIGADE,** IN THE SOUTHWEST, HALFWAY ACROSS THE COUNTRY TOWARDS NEW YORK!

CALLING THE **FANTASTIC FOUR! CONDITION RED!** CONTACT **TEEN BRIGADE!! HULK** MUST BE FOUND!! DO YOU READ ME?

4.

BUT THE SINISTER GOD OF EVIL HAS *OTHER* PLANS...

THE *FANTASTIC FOUR* WILL RUIN EVERYTHING! IT IS *THOR* I WANT!...NO ONE ELSE! I MUST TAKE INSTANT ACTION!

THERE! I HAVE USED MY MENTAL POWERS TO JAM THE RADIO WAVES, DIVERTING THEM TO A DIFFERENT WAVE-LENGTH...ONE WHICH I KNOW *DON BLAKE* IS LISTENING TO!

AND, IN THE QUIET STUDY OF DR. BLAKE...

...CONTACT *TEEN BRIGADE!* HULK MUST BE FOUND! DO YOU READ US?

STRANGE! SOUNDS LIKE A CALL FOR *THOR!*

THE *TEEN BRIGADE!* THEY'RE LOCATED IN THE SOUTH-WEST! IF THIS CONCERNS THE *HULK,* IT MUST BE SERIOUS! AND SO, THE TIME HAS COME...

...FOR DR. DON BLAKE TO STRIKE HIS ENCHANTED CANE ONCE UPON THE FLOOR, CASTING OFF HIS MORTAL GUISE, AND BECOMING...

...THE MIGHTY *THOR,* GOD OF *THUNDER!*

BUT, UNSUSPECTED BY *LOKI,* OTHERS HAVE *ALSO* HEARD THE RADIO MESSAGE, AND THOUGHT IT WAS BEAMED TO THEM! AMONG THEM ARE THE ASTONISHING *ANT-MAN* AND THE *WASP!*

WAIT FOR *ME, ANT-MAN!*

I THOUGHT YOU WEREN'T COMING, JAN!

I CAN'T SEE WHY YOU HAVE TO STOP AND POWDER YOUR NOSE EVERY TIME WE HAVE A MISSION!

HENRY PYM, YOU'RE BEGIN-NING TO SOUND LIKE A STUFFY OLD *BACHELOR* AGAIN!

AND I INTEND TO *REMAIN* THAT WAY! NOW SEE IF YOU CAN'T BE QUIET LONG ENOUGH FOR ME TO ACTIVATE THE DOUBLE CATAPULT!

BUT WHY DO *I* HAVE TO USE YOUR SILLY FLYING ANT RELAYS? I HAPPEN TO HAVE MY *OWN* WINGS!

BUT WE'VE GOT A *THOUSAND* MILES TO COVER, JAN, AND I DON'T WANT YOU EXHAUSTED WHEN WE GET THERE!

5.

AND STILL *ANOTHER* PAIR OF EARS HAVE INTERCEPTED THE URGENT BROADCAST...THE EARS OF *ANTHONY STARK*, MILLIONAIRE INDUSTRIALIST AND PLAYBOY...BETTER KNOWN TO THE UNSUSPECTING WORLD AS *IRON MAN!*

LUCKY I WAS TUNED IN TO THE RIGHT FREQUENCY! THINGS HAVE BEEN TOO DULL AROUND HERE LATELY!

I'VE ALWAYS *WONDERED* WHETHER THE *HULK* REALLY EXISTED, AND WHETHER *IRON MAN'S* STRENGTH WAS A MATCH FOR HIM!

LOOKS AS THOUGH I'LL GET A CHANCE TO FIND OUT! SOONER THAN I THOUGHT!

I'LL PROPEL MYSELF FOR MOST OF THE TRIP BY MY SOLAR BATTERY! IT'S SLOWER THAN MY TRANSISTORS, BUT IT LASTS LONGER...AND I'VE GOT A LONG WAY TO GO!

THEN, AFTER A FEW HOURS OF CROSS-COUNTRY FLYING...

ALMOST THERE! NOW TO SWITCH TO MY TRANSISTORS BEFORE I LULL MYSELF TO SLEEP UP HERE!

AHHH! THIS IS MORE *LIKE* IT!

MEANWHILE, IN THE MAIN CLUBROOM OF THE *TEEN BRIGADE*, A FEELING OF *GLOOM* FILLS THE AIR...

STILL NO WORD FROM THE FF, EH?

GUESS THEY NEVER GOT THE MESSAGE!

OR ELSE THEY CAN'T BE BOTHERED TO ANSWER A BUNCH OF KIDS LIKE US!

HEY! HOLD IT, YOU GUYS! *CLAM UP!* I'M GETTIN' SOMETHIN'...IT..IT'S *MR. FANTASTIC!*

WELL, C'MON, RICK... *GIVE!!* WHAT DOES HE *SAY?* LET US IN ON IT!!

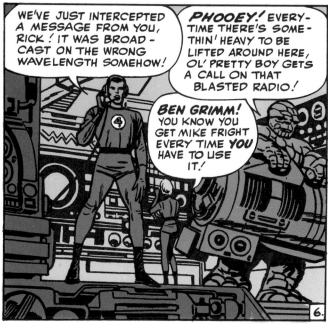

WE'VE JUST INTERCEPTED A MESSAGE FROM YOU, RICK! IT WAS BROADCAST ON THE WRONG WAVELENGTH SOMEHOW!

PHOOEY! EVERYTIME THERE'S SOMETHIN' HEAVY TO BE LIFTED AROUND HERE, OL' PRETTY BOY GETS A CALL ON THAT BLASTED RADIO!

BEN GRIMM! YOU KNOW YOU GET MIKE FRIGHT EVERY TIME *YOU* HAVE TO USE IT!

6.

WE'RE WRAPPED UP IN ANOTHER CASE NOW, SON, BUT...

..ACCORDING TO MY CALCULATIONS, YOUR MESSAGE SHOULD BE PICKED UP BY SOME OTHERS WHO CAN HELP YOU! IF YOU DON'T GET HELP SOON, RADIO BACK AND LET ME KNOW!

YOU KIDDIN', REED? WHO ELSE COULD EVER DO WHAT WE CAN DO?

THEN, AS THE CONTACT IS BROKEN, AS IF IN ANSWER TO THE HUMAN TORCH'S BANTERING QUESTION...

LOOKS LIKE WE STRUCK OUT, RICK! THE FF CAN'T MAKE IT, HUH?

WONDER WHAT HE MEANT ABOUT SOMEONE ELSE MAYBE HELPIN' US?

AW, JUST SOME BUCK-PASSIN', THAT'S ALL!

H-HEY, GUYS... LOOK!

WHY SO SURPRISED? DIDN'T YOU SEND FOR ME?

WOWEE! IT'S THOR!!

LOOK! FLYIN' ABOVE US! IT'S ANT-MAN AND THE WASP!

IT WOULD SEEM AS THOUGH THE GANG'S ALL HERE, EH, LADS?

HENRY! DID YOU SEE THAT GORGEOUS THOR?! HOW CAN I EVER MAKE HIM NOTICE ME?

STOP ACTING LIKE A LOVESICK FEMALE AND SLIP BEHIND THIS LENS WITH ME! I'LL ADJUST IT SO IT'LL PROJECT OUR IMAGES ON THE WALL!

WE HEARD THAT YOU NEEDED HELP, BOYS! IT CERTAINLY LOOKS AS THOUGH YOU'RE GOING TO GET IT!

THIS IS THE COOLEST! FIRST THOR, THEN IRON MAN, AND NOW ANT-MAN AND THE WASP! IT'S MORE THAN WE DARED HOPE FOR!

7.

BUT, BACK IN ASGARD...

BAH! THIS COMPLICATES THINGS FOR ME! I ONLY WANT TO FIND A WAY TO LURE THOR UP HERE! I AM NOT INTERESTED IN THOSE OTHERS!

THOR IS AT THE WINDOW NOW! IF I MOVE QUICKLY, I MAY STILL SUCCEED! I'LL CREATE A MENTAL IMAGE OF THE HULK AND MAKE IT RUN PAST THOR'S FIELD OF VISION!

I THOUGHT I SAW... IT IS! IT'S THE HULK!

NO NEED FOR ME TO DISTURB THE OTHERS!

NO MATTER HOW FAST HE CAN LEAP, I CAN ALWAYS FOLLOW HIM!...

...BY HURLING MY MIGHTY HAMMER AND HOLDING ONTO THE UNBREAKABLE THONG!

STRANGE! HE MOVES AS THOUGH HE HASN'T SEEN ME...AS THOUGH HE IS UNAWARE OF ANYTHING!

NO! NOW HE SEES ME! HE IS GRASPING THAT HUGE BOULDER! HE INTENDS TO HURL IT AT ME! BUT MY HAMMER WILL STOP HIM!

IMPOSSIBLE! IT... IT WENT RIGHT THROUGH HIM!

NOW HE'S FADING AWAY! IT ISN'T THE HULK AT ALL! MERELY A MENTAL IMAGE!

ONLY LOKI IS CAPABLE OF SUCH WIZARDRY! I SHOULD HAVE SUSPECTED! HE MUST BE BEHIND IT!

8.

LOKI, THOU EVIL ONE! I KNOW NOT WHAT YOUR PLAN IS, BUT I HAVE WARNED YOU NEVER TO MEDDLE IN EARTH AFFAIRS! AND NOW YOU DARE DEFY ME!

I HAVE SUCCEEDED! HE IS RETURNING TO ASGARD! BUT WHEN HE REACHES THE ISLE OF SILENCE, IT IS I WHO SHALL EMERGE THE VICTOR!... FOR THIS TIME I AM READY FOR THE COMING OF THOR!

BUT, BACK ON EARTH, THE WHEELS SET IN MOTION BY VILLAINOUS LOKI CANNOT BE STOPPED! THE HULK IS STILL AT LARGE... AND OUR AMAZING SAGA HAS BARELY BEGUN!

THOR HAS DISAPPEARED! BUT DON'T WORRY, LAD!... I'M SURE THAT ANT-MAN AND I WILL BE ABLE TO FIND THE HULK AND TO LEARN THE TRUTH!

IF HE REALLY IS ON A RAMPAGE, LOOK OUT!! HE'S STRONGER THAN ANYONE EVEN SUSPECTS! BUT IF HE'S INNOCENT, HE MUST NOT BE HURT... UNDERSTAND?

MEANWHILE, WHERE IS THE INCREDIBLE HULK? HUNTED, HOUNDED, BEWILDERED, HE HAS TAKEN REFUGE WITH A TRAVELING CIRCUS, AS HE WONDERS WHAT TO DO NEXT!

THERE HE IS LADIES AND GENTLEMEN... MECHANO, THE MOST POWERFUL, LIFELIKE ROBOT ON EARTH! HE WALKS LIKE A MAN, HE MOVES LIKE A MAN, BUT HE IS AS STRONG AS A DOZEN BULLDOZERS! MECHANO, THE MARVEL OF THE AGE!!

9.

10.

11.

MEANWHILE, THE AUDIENCE, THINKING IT IS ALL PART OF THE SHOW, HOWLS WITH UNRESTRAINED ENTHUSIASM...

BEST DURN ACT I EVER SAW!

THAT BIG ROBOT HAS THE DISPOSITION OF MY BROTHER-IN-LAW!

HOW DO THEY EVER DREAM THESE THINGS UP?

SO! YOU REFUSE TO STOP??

YOU INTEND TO KEEP HOUNDING ME, DO YOU?

ALL RIGHT, THE MASQUERADE'S OVER! I DON'T CARE WHO KNOWS WHO I AM! SOON AS I WIPE THIS STUPID MAKE-UP OFF, I'M GONNA RIP THIS PLACE APART WITH MY BARE HANDS! WHAT HAVE I GOT TO FEAR! NOTHING CAN HURT THE HULK!

THEN, AS THE STARTLED, INCREDULOUS AUDIENCE RECOILS IN PANIC...

WE'VE DONE IT! WE'VE BROUGHT HIM OUT INTO THE OPEN! NOW EVERY SECOND COUNTS! LURE HIM UNDER THE TRAPEZE NET! I'LL DO THE REST!

DON'T LET ME DOWN, HENRY! I WOULDN'T WANT HIM FOR A PERMANENT PLAYMATE!

THE INSECT-WOMAN AGAIN! WHY DO YOU BUZZ AROUND ME?? YOU MUST BE AN ENEMY! I CAN FEEL IT!

HOW CAN ANYONE SO BIG MOVE SO FAST? HE'S THE MOST DREADFUL THING I'VE EVER SEEN!

YOU THINK YOU CAN ESCAPE ME BECAUSE OF YOUR SIZE? NO ONE ESCAPES THE HULK!

OHHH...

THAT BELLOWS! FEELS LIKE A HURRICANE! ≶GASP!≶ CAN'T BREATHE! CAN'T SEE....OUT OF CONTROL! HENRY... HELP!!

NO ONE CAN SAVE YOU NOW!

12.

SUDDENLY, A MASSIVE GOLDEN FIGURE BREAKS THROUGH THE CROWD OF AMAZED SPECTATORS, AND THE SHOCK OF SEEING *IRON MAN* CHARGING TOWARDS HIM MAKES THE *HULK* TEMPORARILY FORGET HIS TINY PRISONER!

YOU'RE *WRONG!* THERE IS *ONE* WHO CAN SAVE HER!

IRON MAN!

THROUGH HIS TRANSISTOR-POWERED, BUILT-IN RADIO RECEIVER, THE GOLDEN WARRIOR HEARS A TERSE REPORT FROM NEARBY *ANT-MAN!*

PERFECT TIMING, *IRON MAN!* NOW, QUICKLY... MAKE HIM RUN TOWARD THE CENTER OF THE ARENA! I'VE PREPARED A TRAP FOR HIM! LET HIM TRY TO ESCAPE BY LEAPING THROUGH THE TOP OF THE TENT!

AND, AS THE *HULK* EXECUTES ONE OF HIS INCREDIBLE LEAPS, CRASHING THROUGH THE VERY TOP OF THE CIRCUS TENT...

ARGHH!

HE HIT THE SPECIAL NYLON SAFETY NETTING WHICH MY ANTS SPREAD OVER THE TOP OF THE TENT! NOW IF IT WILL ONLY HOLD HIM LONG ENOUGH!

BUT CAN ANY MERE NYLON NETTING BE STRONG ENOUGH TO HOLD THE RAMPAGING, EXPLODING HUMAN POWERHOUSE THAT IS THE *HULK*? WITH A MIGHTY SURGE OF BRUTE FORCE HE HURLS HIMSELF UPWARD, TAKING ALL THE NETTING AND THE ENTIRE TENT WITH HIM!

HE'S GETTING *AWAY!!*

NEVER HAVE HUMAN EYES BEHELD SUCH AN AWESOME SPECTACLE... NEVER HAS MORTAL MAN WITNESSED SUCH A STUPENDOUS SIGHT!!

SECONDS LATER, HAVING RIPPED OFF THE ENTANGLING FABRICS ON THE SHAGGY PEAKS NEARBY, THE *HULK* CONTINUES HIS FRENZIED FLIGHT... WITH A LONE PURSUER!

THERE IS NO PLACE ON EARTH WHERE I CANNOT FOLLOW YOU!

13.

SUDDENLY, THE MIGHTY FUGITIVE DROPS TO EARTH, AS HIS GOLDEN PURSUER, UNABLE TO STOP IN TIME, WHIZZES OVER HIM!

THEN, WITH THE SPEED OF A CHARGING DREADNOUGHT, THE *HULK* LEAPS INTO THE AIR AGAIN, BEHIND THE STARTLED *IRON MAN!*

IN A TRICE THE HUNTED HAS BECOME THE HUNTER, AS A THUNDEROUS BLOW TO HIS POWER-PACK DAMAGES *IRON MAN'S* PROPULSION BATTERY!

NO ONE CAN STOP THE *HULK!*

CAN'T GO AFTER HIM TILL I REPAIR MY BATTERY!

HULK... WAIT! I WANT TO *HELP* YOU! TRUST ME! YOU CAN'T REMAIN A FUGITIVE *FOREVER!* COME BACK!!

BAH! I DON'T TRUST *ANYBODY!*

MEANWHILE, WHAT OF THE MIGHTY *THOR?* AT THAT MOMENT, IN THE GRAND CHAMBER OF THE IMPERIAL PALACE AT ASGARD...

NOBLE ODIN, LORD OF GODS! GRANT THY SON PERMISSION TO VISIT *LOKI* ON THE ISLE OF SILENCE, THAT I MAY LEARN IF HE IS RESPONSIBLE FOR SOME DEVILTRY ON EARTH!

WE GRANT THEE PERMISSION, BELOVED *THOR!* BUT HARK TO THESE WORDS...

THOUGH *YOU* BE THE SON OF MY HEART.. *LOKI* TOO IS MY SON! I CANNOT INTERFERE IN WHAT TRANSPIRES BETWEEN YOU!

I UNDERSTAND, FATHER!

AND SO, ALONE IN THE NIGHT, THE MIGHTY THUNDER-GOD SETS OUT ACROSS THE SEA OF MIST... AWARE THAT THE ENEMY HE SEEKS IS ALSO A LEGENDARY GOD... AND THE MOST SINISTER, THE MOST DANGEROUS OF ALL!

LOKI MUST KNOW I AM COMING! HE MUST HAVE SET MANY TRAPS FOR ME! BUT I DARE NOT TURN BACK ...NO MATTER WHAT THE RISK!

14

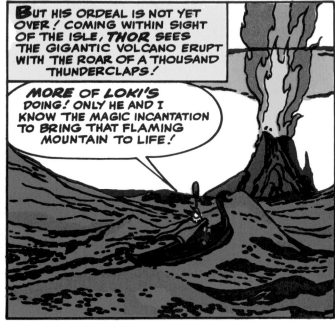

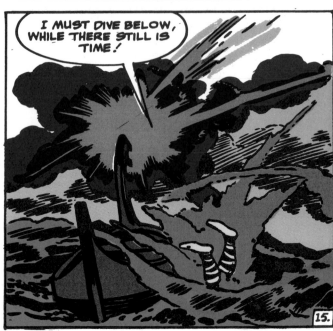

15.

YOU HAVE BEEN AWAY FROM ASGARD SO LONG THAT YOU MIGHT HAVE FORGOTTEN, *THOR*... HERE WE ARE *ALL* IMMORTALS... WE ARE *ALL* SUPER-POWERFUL!

AND NOTHING THAT LIVES, IN ASGARD OR ON EARTH, CAN BREAK THE GRIP OF A *TROLL!* IT IS FROM *THEM* THAT THE EARTH LEGEND OF THE "OLD MAN OF THE SEA" WAS BORN!

THIS IS THE TRAP I PLANNED FOR YOU, *THOR!* I PROMISED THE *TROLLS* THAT, IF THEY OBEYED ME, I WOULD DELIVER THE *MIGHTIEST* OF THE GODS TO THEM! NOW THEY'LL DRAG YOU BELOW, WHERE YOU SHALL SLAVE IN THEIR MINES FOREVER!

NOT *YET*, EVIL ONE! NOT WHILE I HAVE ONE HAND FREE AND CAN STILL POUND MY ENCHANTED MALLET ON THE GROUND!

FOR, REMEMBER... I AM STILL GOD OF THE THUNDER, AND THE BLAZING LIGHTNING!

LIGHTNING SO *BRIGHT* THAT THE SENSITIVE EYES OF A *TROLL*, USED TO DWELLING IN SEMI-DARKNESS, CANNOT *BEAR* IT!

AND NOW THAT HE HAS FLED BACK TO THE STYGIAN DEPTHS FROM WHENCE HE CAME, IT IS TIME FOR *YOU* TO TASTE THE AWESOME VENGEANCE OF *THOR!*

STOP, THUNDER GOD! YOU HAVE NOT DEFEATED *LOKI* YET!

I-I SWUNG MY HAMMER RIGHT *THROUGH* YOU!

NOT THROUGH *ME*, FOOL! THROUGH A MENTAL *IMAGE* OF ME! REMEMBER, *LOKI* CAN MATCH YOU, TRICK FOR TRICK, AND *THEN* SOME!

17.

19.

21.

IN THE MAIN STUDY OF AN EXCLUSIVE PRIVATE SCHOOL IN NEW YORK'S WESTCHESTER COUNTY, A STRANGE SILENT MAN SITS MOTIONLESS, BROODING...ALONE WITH HIS INDESCRIBABLE THOUGHTS...

FINALLY, HIS MEDITATION COMES TO AN END! THEN, WHILE HE REMAINS COMPLETELY MOTIONLESS, A SHARP, COMMANDING THOUGHT RINGS OUT, ECHOING THROUGH THE GREAT HALLS OF THE BUILDING!

ATTENTION, X-MEN! THIS IS PROFESSOR XAVIER CALLING! REPEAT: THIS IS PROFESSOR X CALLING!

YOU ARE ORDERED TO APPEAR AT ONCE! CLASS IS NOW IN SESSION! TARDINESS WILL BE PUNISHED!

NEVER, WITHIN THE MEMORY OF MAN, WAS THERE A "CLASS" SUCH AS THIS! NEVER WAS THERE A "TEACHER" SUCH AS PROFESSOR X! AND NEVER WERE THERE "STUDENTS" SUCH AS THE...

X-MEN

CYCLOPS PRESENT AND ACCOUNTED FOR, SIR!

THE ANGEL REPORTING, SIR!

ICEMAN RIGHT ON SCHEDULE, SIR!

THE BEAST IS HERE, SIR!

Written by: STAN LEE
Drawn by: JACK KIRBY
Inked by: PAUL REINMAN
Lettered by: S. ROSEN

X-401

AND NOW, PREPARE YOURSELF FOR ONE OF THE MOST EXCITING READING EXPERIENCES OF YOUR LIFE! FOR YOU ARE ABOUT TO ENTER THE FASCINATING, UNPREDICTABLE WORLD OF...THE X-MEN!

2.

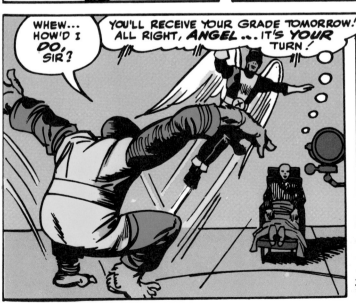

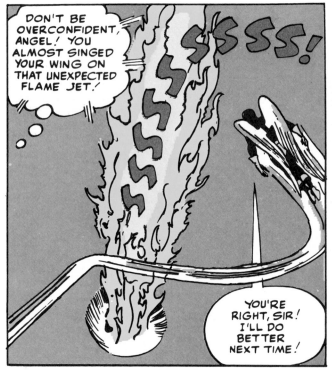

5.

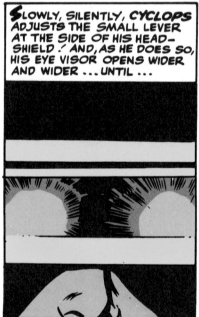

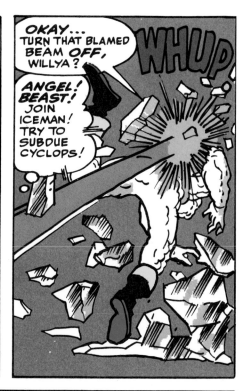

7.

YOU'RE *RIGHT,* SIR! *WOW!* SHE'S A *REAL LIVING DOLL!*

A *REDHEAD!* LOOK AT THAT *FACE...* AND THE *REST* OF HER!

ALL OF A SUDDEN, I'M IN NO HURRY TO GRADUATE FROM THIS PLACE!

A GIRL... *BIG DEAL!* I'M GLAD I'M NOT A WOLF LIKE *YOU* GUYS!

I'M GLAD, *TOO!* WHO NEEDS THE EXTRA COMPETITION FROM ICEMAN?!

I WONDER WHAT SUPER-HUMAN POWERS *SHE* POSSESSES! SHE LOOKS NORMAL ENOUGH!

WELL, LET'S GO IN AND CHANGE, SO WE DON'T SCARE HER WHEN SHE FIRST SEES US!

COME IN, MY CHILD! I AM *PROFESSOR XAVIER!* I AM GLAD YOU RECEIVED MY MESSAGE!

IT ALL SEEMED SO STRANGE, PROFESSOR, AND SO... MYSTERIOUS! I WAS TO TELL NO ONE BUT MY PARENTS THAT I'M COMING HERE... AND YOU DIDN'T DESCRIBE THE COURSE OF STUDY!

WHAT KIND OF SCHOOL *IS* THIS, SIR? I HAVE A RIGHT TO KNOW!

I THINK YOU *ALREADY* SUSPECT, MISS GREY! YOU SEE, I CAN READ YOUR THOUGHTS QUITE CLEARLY... AND I KNOW ALL ABOUT YOUR UNUSUAL "TALENT"!

YOU, MISS GREY, LIKE THE OTHER FOUR STUDENTS AT THIS MOST EXCLUSIVE SCHOOL, ARE A *MUTANT!* YOU POSSESS AN *EXTRA* POWER.. ONE WHICH ORDINARY HUMANS DO *NOT!!* THAT IS WHY I CALL MY STUDENTS ... *X-MEN,* FOR *EX*-TRA POWER!

AND HERE THEY ARE NOW! ALLOW ME TO PRESENT THEM TO YOU! FROM LEFT TO RIGHT WE HAVE *HANK McCOY,* KNOWN TO US AS *THE BEAST!* BOBBY DRAKE, NICKNAMED *ICEMAN!* *SLIM SUMMERS,* OUR HUMAN *CYCLOPS!* AND *WARREN WORTHINGTON THE THIRD,* WHO IS CALLED THE *ANGEL!* BOYS, THIS IS *MISS JEAN GREY!* SHE WILL BE KNOWN AS *MARVEL GIRL!*

WELCOME TO THE X-MEN, MISS GREY!

8.

HOW COME HE'S CALLING YOU *MARVEL GIRL*, MISS GREY? WHAT POWER DO YOU HAVE?

SHE HAS *ONE* VERY OBVIOUS POWER... THE POWER TO MAKE A MAN'S *HEART* BEAT FASTER!

Y'KNOW SOMETHING, WARREN, IF I HAD *YOUR* LINE, I'D *SHOOT MYSELF!*

YOU'LL LEARN MORE ABOUT ME, BOYS, IN TIME!

WELL, NO TIME LIKE THE PRESENT! C'MON, SLIM, BRING THE LITTLE LADY A CHAIR!

HANK, I'D BRING HER THE WHOLE ROOM OF FURNITURE IF SHE ASKED ME!

THAT'S REALLY NOT NECESSARY, SLIM!

TH..THE CHAIR! IT SLID OUT OF MY HANDS!

Y!!!!!! HOLY SMOKE! WHAT'S GOIN' *ON?!!*

DON'T BE ALARMED, BOYS! I JUST THOUGHT I'D SAVE YOU THE TROUBLE!

ZZIP?

NOW, THEN, PROFESSOR, I BELIEVE WE CAN CONTINUE OUR INTER- VIEW! AS YOU WERE SAYING...

I DON'T *GET* IT, SIR! WHAT HAPPENED TO THAT MOVING CHAIR??

PERHAPS YOU'D BETTER DEMONSTRATE A BIT *MORE*, JEAN!

VERY WELL, SIR! ALL MY LIFE I'VE HAD TO *CONCEAL* THIS POWER OF MINE...

NOW, I MUST ADMIT IT'S A PLEASURE TO BE ABLE TO PRACTICE *TELEKINESIS* OPENLY, WITHOUT FEAR OF BEING DISCOVERED! OBSERVE THAT BOOK!

BY THE POWER OF THOUGHT, I AM ABLE TO MOVE OBJECTS AT WILL!

BUT IT GETS BORING AFTER A WHILE, SO I'LL RETURN THE BOOK... LIKE THIS!

9.

THANK YOU, JEAN! AND NOW LET ME TELL YOU MORE ABOUT MY SCHOOL...

I WAS BORN OF PARENTS WHO HAD WORKED ON THE FIRST A-BOMB PROJECT! LIKE YOURSELVES, I AM A *MUTANT*... POSSIBLY THE *FIRST* SUCH MUTANT! I HAVE THE POWER TO READ MINDS, AND TO PROJECT MY OWN THOUGHTS INTO THE BRAINS OF OTHERS!

BUT, WHEN I WAS YOUNG, NORMAL PEOPLE FEARED ME, DISTRUSTED ME! I REALIZED THE HUMAN RACE IS NOT YET READY TO *ACCEPT* THOSE WITH EXTRA POWERS! SO I DECIDED TO BUILD A HAVEN... A SCHOOL FOR *X-MEN!*

HERE WE STAY, UNSUSPECTED BY NORMAL HUMANS, AS WE LEARN TO USE OUR POWERS FOR THE BENEFIT OF MANKIND... TO HELP THOSE WHO WOULD DISTRUST US IF THEY KNEW OF OUR EXISTENCE!

DUE TO A CHILDHOOD ACCIDENT, I MYSELF MUST REMAIN IN THIS CHAIR, BUT THROUGH A MASTER CONTROL PANEL I HAVE MANY DEVICES AT MY COMMAND... AND THROUGH MY *MIND*, I AM ALWAYS IN TOUCH WITH MY *X-MEN!*

AND NOW, I LEAVE YOU TO GET TO KNOW EACH OTHER BETTER!

LET ME BE THE FIRST TO WELCOME YOU TO THE *X-MEN*, BEAUTIFUL! MMMMM!

OH!

HANK! TAKE YOUR PAWS OFF HER!

FOR THE LUVVA PETE!

OH! *BOY!* WHAT A *GAL!* I HOPE SHE KEEPS THAT BIG APE UP THERE *FOREVER!*

DON'T WORRY, WARREN! I'M NOT EXACTLY *HELPLESS*, AS YOU CAN SEE!

HEY, C'MON! HAVE A HEART! I WAS ONLY TRYING TO BE *FRIENDLY!*

A FELLA COULD GET *DIZZY* UP HERE! LEMME DOWN, HUH? THIS IS EMBARRASSING!

VERY WELL, I'LL LET YOU DOWN!

THERE! YOU'RE DOWN!

WHUMP!

OOOFF!!

10.

I HOPE I WASN'T TOO ROUGH ON THE POOR DEAR!

NOT AT ALL, JEAN! WE DON'T USE KID GLOVES HERE! WE HAVE TO MAKE OUR TRAINING AS ROUGH AS POSSIBLE, TO PREPARE OUR-SELVES FOR OUR MISSION IN THE OUTSIDE WORLD!

THAT'S WHAT I'VE WANTED TO ASK! JUST WHAT EXACTLY IS OUR REAL MISSION, SIR?

JEAN, THERE ARE MANY MUTANTS WALK-ING THE EARTH... AND MORE ARE BORN EACH YEAR!

NOT ALL OF THEM WANT TO HELP MANKIND!...SOME HATE THE HUMAN RACE, AND WISH TO DESTROY IT! SOME FEEL THAT THE MUTANTS SHOULD BE THE REAL RULERS OF EARTH! IT IS OUR JOB TO PROTECT MANKIND FROM THOSE... FROM THE EVIL MUTANTS!

AT THAT VERY MOMENT, JUST SUCH A MUTANT PREPARES TO STRIKE... IN A SECRET LABORA-TORY NEAR CAPE CITADEL!

THE MOMENT IS AT HAND!

ALL MY MONTHS OF PREPARATION AND PLANNING SHALL NOW PAY OFF!

THE HUMAN RACE NO LONGER DESERVES DOMINION OVER THE PLANET EARTH! THE DAY OF THE MUTANTS IS UPON US!

THE FIRST PHASE OF MY PLAN SHALL BE TO SHOW MY POWER...TO MAKE HOMO SAPIENS BOW TO HOMO SUPERIOR!

THE MIGHTIEST ROCKET OF ALL IS ABOUT TO BE LAUNCHED! USING MAXIMUM SECURITY PRECAUTIONS, THE GOVERNMENT FEELS NOTHING CAN PREVENT ITS SUCCESSFUL FLIGHT!

BUT HERE, MILES FROM THE LAUNCH-ING SITE, I, THE MIRACULOUS MAGNETO, ALONE SHALL MAKE A MOCKERY OF THEIR GREATEST EFFORT!

11.

AHHH! I CAN FEEL THE IRRESISTABLE WAVES OF PURE MAGNETIC ENERGY SURGING FROM ME! NOW, BY EXERTING EVERY IOTA OF POWER, I CAN *DIRECT* THAT ENERGY UPWARD... UPWARD...

...UNTIL IT STRIKES THE SPEEDING MISSILE, CAUSING IT TO CHANGE DIRECTION...TO FALTER...TO LOSE ALTITUDE!

...TO BE COMPLETELY, IRREVOCABLY *DESTROYED!!*

GENERAL, EVERY PHASE OF THE LAUNCHING WAS A-OKAY! THERE CAN ONLY BE *ONE* EXPLANATION... THE BIRD WAS *TAMPERED WITH!*

BUT *HOW?* EVEN A *MICROBE* COULDN'T HAVE PENETRATED OUR TOP SECRET SECURITY MEASURES!

THE NEXT DAY, THE SHOCKING NEWS IS TRANSMITTED TO A STARTLED PUBLIC...

INCREDIBLE! IT'S ALMOST AS THOUGH A DESTRUCTIVE *GHOST* IS RUNNING AMOK AT THE CAPE!

EXTRA! EXTRA! ANOTHER MISSILE FAILS! EXTRA!

DAILY GLOBE — FINAL

SIXTH TOP SECRET LAUNCHING FAILS AT SEA!

PHANTOM SABOTEUR STRIKES AGAIN!

BUT THE WORST IS YET TO COME! LATER THAT AFTERNOON, AT THE HEAVILY GUARDED FENCE SURROUNDING THE LAUNCHING SITE...

KEEP THAT GUN *STEADY!* WHY IS IT *QUIVERING* THAT WAY?

W-WE'RE NOT DOIN' IT, SIR! IT..IT'S MOVIN' BY *ITSELF!!*

SUDDENLY, LIKE A LIVING THING, THE MACHINE GUN LEAPS INTO THE AIR, SPINS AROUND, AND BEGINS TO FIRE WILDLY IN ALL DIRECTIONS!

RUN FOR COVER!! THE GUN IS OUT OF CONTROL!!

12.

BUT, THE MACHINE GUN IS NOT THE *ONLY* THING THAT SUDDENLY, MADDENINGLY SEEM TO GO AMOK!

RUN! THE TANK IS MOVING BY *ITSELF!* GANGWAY!

IT..IT'S *IMPOSSIBLE!* AND YET...IT'S ACTING LIKE IT HAS A MIND OF ITS OWN! LIKE IT'S *TRYING* TO MENACE US!

SWISH!

CLANK!

CLANK!

WITHIN SECONDS, THE ENTIRE INSTALLATION IS ALARMED, AS EMERGENCY MEASURES ARE SWIFTLY BROUGHT INTO PLAY! AND THEN...

SOUND THE ALARM! *CONDITION RED!* ALERT THE PENTAGON!

GENERAL! *LOOK!* ABOVE US...IN THE SKY!

APPEARING AS THOUGH BY MAGIC, OVER THE HEADS OF THE ASTONISHED TROOPS, HUGE LETTERS TAKE SHAPE...COMPOSED OF THE DUST PARTICLES FROM THE AIR ITSELF, SKILLFULLY MAGNETIZED INTO A MESSAGE BY THE UNSEEN MUTANT!

SURRENDER THE BASE OR I'LL TAKE IT BY FORCE!

Magneto

MAGNETO? WHO... *WHAT* IS MAGNETO??

GENERAL, WHAT DOES IT *MEAN?* IS SOMEONE PLAYING A GRIM *PRANK?*

YOU SAW THAT MACHINE GUN... THAT TANK... RAMPAGING OUT OF CONTROL! THIS IS *NO JOKE,* COLONEL!

THEY ARE STARTLED! *GOOD!* THE ELEMENT OF SURPRISE IS IN MY FAVOR!

BUT THEY'RE MAKING NO MOVE TO SURRENDER! PERHAPS THEY NEED *ANOTHER* DEMONSTRATION OF MY POWER!

I'LL DIRECT MY MAGNETIC IMPULSES INTO THIS ENERGIZER, TO INCREASE THEIR POWER, AND THEN I'LL LEAVE THE HELPLESS HOMO SAPIENS WITH NO ROOM FOR DOUBT!

13,

AN INSTANT LATER, INVISIBLE WAVES OF PURE, POWERFUL MAGNETIC ENERGY FLOW IRRESISTIBLY INTO AN UNDERGROUND SILO WHERE ONE OF DEMOCRACY'S SILENT SENTINELS WAIT, AT THE READY!

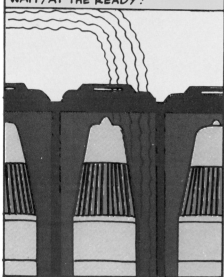

AND THEN, MANIPULATED BY A SINISTER INTELLIGENCE, MANY HUNDREDS OF YARDS AWAY, THE MAGNETIC FORCE LIFTS THE SILO HEAD, ACTIVATING THE MIGHTY MISSILE!!

DEMONSTRATING A POWER WHICH THE HUMAN BRAIN IS ALMOST UNABLE TO COMPREHEND, MAGNETO CAUSES THE GRIM ROCKET TO FALL INTO THE SEA MANY MILES FROM SHORE, NEXT TO AN UNMANNED TARGET SHIP!

BUT STILL, THE THOUGHT OF SURRENDER NEVER CROSSES THE MINDS OF THE FIGHTING-MAD BASE PERSONNEL!

SERGEANT! ORDER THE GUARD DOUBLED AT EVERY MISSILE CONTROL CENTER! ANY ROCKET DEEMED A MENACE IS TO BE DESTROYED INSTANTLY!

SOME POWER BEYOND OUR UNDERSTANDING IS AFFECTING OUR WEAPONS! WE MUST FIND THIS MAGNETO!

GENERAL, LOOK! THAT COMMOTION AT THE MAIN GATE! IT SEEMS THAT HE HAS FOUND US FIRST!

HOLD IT, MAC! IF YOU'RE LOOKIN' FOR A MASQUERADE PARTY, YOU'VE COME TO THE WRONG PLACE! BEAT IT!

WELL SAID, GUARD! WHAT A PITY YOU HAVE NO POWER TO BACK UP SUCH IMPRESSIVE WORDS! YOUR PUNY WEAPONS CANNOT STOP ME!

THEY CAN'T, EH? ONE LITTLE BURST OVER YOUR HEAD WILL SURELY CHANGE YOUR MIND!

I CAN'T EVEN LIFT MY GUN! FEELS LIKE IT WEIGHS A TON!

HEY! WHA—WHAT GIVES? THE GUN WON'T FIRE! THE TRIGGER SEEMS LOCKED IN PLACE!

14.

15.

AS FOR **ME**, IT'LL BE A PLEASURE TO GET OUT OF THIS HARNESS I HAVE TO WEAR!

HAVING A PAIR OF WINGS CAN BE MORE TROUBLE THAN YOU'D GUESS!

THESE RESTRAINING BELTS OF MINE KEEP MY WINGS FROM BULGING UNDER MY SUIT, BUT AFTER A WHILE THEY FEEL LIKE I'M WEARING A **STRAIT-JACKET!**

AHHH! THAT'S MORE LIKE IT! NOW I FEEL LIKE MYSELF AGAIN! NOW THE **ANGEL** IS READY TO SPREAD HIS WINGS ...AND **FLY!**

BUT THE TIME HAS NOT YET COME FOR THE ANGEL TO FLY! INSTEAD, THE BAND OF **SUPER-HUMAN TEEN-AGERS** ARE **DRIVEN** TO THE AIRPORT IN PROFESSOR XAVIER'S SPECIALLY-BUILT ROLLS ROYCE, WITH ITS DARK-TINTED WINDOWS!

BOY! IT MUSTA TAKEN A HEAP OF GREEN STAMPS TO BY A CHARIOT LIKE THIS!

NO JOKING, PLEASE! CONCENTRATE ON YOUR MISSION! REVIEW YOUR POWERS! YOUR FOE IS CERTAIN TO BE HIGHLY DANGEROUS!

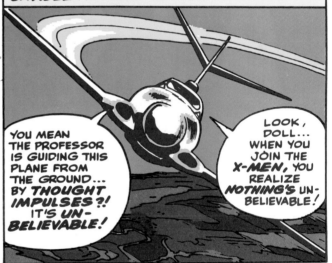

MINUTES LATER, IN THE PROFESSOR'S REMOTE-CONTROL PRIVATE JET, THE **X-MEN** AND **MARVEL GIRL** ARE WINGING TOWARDS **CAPE CITADEL** AT NEARLY THE SPEED OF SOUND!

YOU MEAN THE PROFESSOR IS GUIDING THIS PLANE FROM THE GROUND... BY **THOUGHT IMPULSES?!** IT'S UN-BELIEVABLE!

LOOK, DOLL... WHEN YOU JOIN THE **X-MEN,** YOU REALIZE **NOTHING'S** UN-BELIEVABLE!

A SHORT TIME LATER, AT THE CAPE...

CEASE FIRING! IT'S USELESS! WE HAVEN'T ANYTHING IN OUR ARSENAL THAT'LL PENETRATE **MAGNETO'S** MAGNETIC FORCE FIELD!

TO ALL INTENTS AND PURPOSES, HE'S IN FULL CONTROL OF THE INSTALLATION, WHILE WE'RE ON THE OUTSIDE, LOOKING IN!

WITH DUE RESPECT, GENERAL, I REPRESENT THE **X-MEN!** PERHAPS **WE** CAN HELP!

X-MEN?! WHAT THE..?!

17.

AND NOW, I'LL SWITCH TO *MAXIMUM POWER!* I CAN ONLY MAINTAIN THIS PRESSURE FOR A FEW SECONDS, BUT... *AHH!* I *DID* IT!

BEHIND THE FORCE FIELD, THE NATURAL ENERGY FEED-BACK WEAKENS THE STARTLED MAGNETO!

SOME POWER IS ATTACKING ME! SOME POWER AS SUPER-HUMAN AS MY *OWN!*

I WAS STAGGERED BECAUSE I WAS UN-PREPARED FOR ANY SUCH ONSLAUGHT! BUT NOW THAT I'M FOREWARNED, I CAN DEFEAT *ANY* FOE...NO MATTER *HOW* SUPER-HUMAN HE MAY BE!

BUT MAGNETO IS SOON TO LEARN THAT HE HAS MORE THAN ONE FOE TO CONTEND WITH! HE HAS THE FIGHTING BAND OF X-MEN!

CYCLOPS ALMOST KNOCKED HIM-SELF OUT, BUT HE GOT US *IN* HERE! NOW LET'S PROVE WE CAN CARRY THE BALL!

LOOK SHARP, *X-MEN!* YOU ARE FACING A DANGER-OUS ENEMY!

AHHH! NOW I SEE MY ANTAGONISTS! FIVE COSTUMED YOUTHS! SURELY ALL THEIR POWERS PUT TOGETHER CAN BE NO MATCH FOR *MINE!*

BUT I WILL LET THE BASE'S *HUNTER MISSILES* DO MY FIGHTING FOR ME! THEY WILL HUNT THE FIVE DOWN, ATTRACTED BY THEIR BODY HEAT!

INTERCEPTOR MISSILES

FIRE

AND SO, AT THE PRESS OF A BUTTON, MAGNETO UNLEASHES FIVE OF THE MOST SOPHISTICATED WEAPONS EVER CREATED...ALL ZEROED IN ON THE X-MEN!

19.

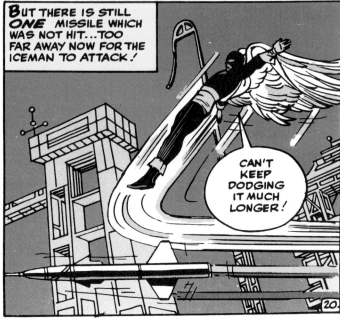

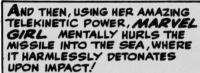

22

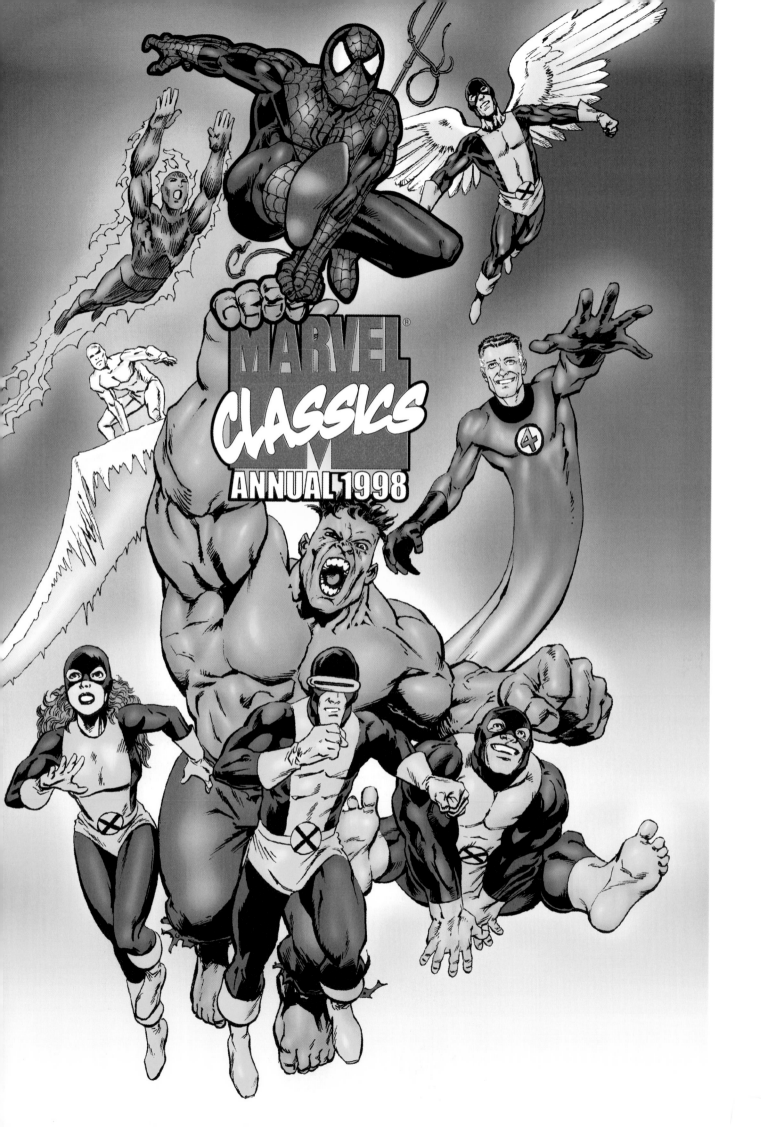